SPAKE

SPAKE

Edited by Urszula Clark and Jonathan Davidson

Nine
Arches
Press

Spake
Edited by Urszula Clark and Jonathan Davidson

ISBN: 978-1-911027-82-9
eISBN: 978-1-911027-83-6

Cover layout by Jane Commane.
Image credits: Watercolour map © werbeantrieb and historic
Birmingham map © bauhaus1000, both via iStock.com.

First published October 2019 by:

Nine Arches Press
Unit 14, Sir Frank Whittle Business Centre,
Great Central Way, Rugby.
CV21 3XH
United Kingdom

www.ninearchespress.com

Printed in the United Kingdom by:
Imprint Digital

Nine Arches Press is supported using public funding
by Arts Council England.

Supported using public funding by
**ARTS COUNCIL
ENGLAND**

Published in partnership with:

Contents

Introduction

For far too long, writing that includes and draws upon features of regional dialects such as those of the English West Midlands has been routinely dismissed, ignored or simply silenced by the gatekeepers of mainstream culture. Editors, for example, may claim dialect is 'off-putting' to their readers or that work that communicates accent is difficult to read. We believe that this should not be the case.

This volume features contemporary writing that draws upon dialect in ways that exploit the potential of the narrative and poetic voice. Many of the pieces bring to life the silent histories and realities of a working class way of life in what was once this country's industrial heartland. Other pieces are entirely contemporary, suggesting that literature in dialect will reflect the future as well as the past. From contemporary re-imaginings of the interwar decades of the 1920s and 1930s in Steven Knight's TV series *Peaky Blinders* to Liz Berry's prize winning poetry and up and coming new talent, this volume celebrates and gives voice to experiences rooted in the region that have largely lain at the margins.

The counties and urban areas that make up the English West Midlands encompass a rich and varied range of accents and dialects. Whilst a rich tradition of poetry and prose written in vernaculars of English exists within mainstream literature, very little of it is from the West Midlands. As Liz Berry points out in her reflective piece, even now Black Country and neighbouring Birmingham voices continue to top the polls as the least liked of all British accents and dialects. 'We may not be thick, but we certainly sound it', writes Paul McDonald, pointing out that there is something about the Birmingham and Black Country accents particularly that suggests this, in much the same way that blues music suggests misery. It is rare to hear, for example, a West

Midlander on national television or radio, except as a comic voice or as a football pundit.

Associated with ignorance and lack of eloquence, it is hardly surprising that writers haven't felt able to bring the region's vernacular to the forefront of literature. Even when a writer such as Lisa Blower draws upon the very distinct Staffordshire Potteries dialect in her work, it does not always make the final draft, with editors claiming to find the dialect off-putting or there being 'problems' with tense. Attitudes towards regional accents and dialects of English are stubborn things, rooted in prejudices that go way back to the seventeenth century, and the ways in which English as a language was standardised, rooted in differences of social class.

In the UK, accent and dialect act as a proxy for social class. Social mobility since the 1970s has increased largely through education, with the corresponding growth of the middle class and shrinking of the working class. We don't notice how we speak until we move outside of our immediate environments, usually by moving to a different town or city to go to college or university or, in the case of someone like Benjamin Zephaniah, to cities such as London or Manchester for the arts scene. If how we speak is 'different', then attention is drawn to this by others, and as Zephaniah acknowledges, he was unaware of being Brummie until he went to London.

This anthology offers a small selection of contemporary writing that is made more authentic and more enjoyable through its use of dialect and accent. Some pieces have been previously published but many have been commissioned especially for this anthology. The anthology also includes some writers from BAME communities, who bring an additional richness to the use of language in the West Midlands. We are particularly grateful to those contributors who have reflected on their use of accent and dialect through short essays, and for the two fascinating interviews with Benjamin Zephaniah and Julie Walters.

Our thanks to all the writers who contributed with such enthusiasm and to various copyright holders for permission to reprint some previously published work. This anthology has been a partnership between Aston University, Writing West Midlands and the publishers Nine Arches Press, and our thanks to colleagues in all three organisations for their support.

Professor Urszula Clark, Aston University
& Jonathan Davidson, Writing West Midlands
Joint Editors

Liz Berry

Homing

For years you kept your accent
in a box beneath the bed,
the lock rusted shut by hours of elocution
how now brown cow
the teacher's ruler across your legs.

We heard it escape sometimes,
a guttural *uh* on the phone to your sister,
saft or *blart* to a taxi driver
unpacking your bags from his boot.
I loved its thick drawl, *g*'s that rang.

Clearing your house, the only thing
I wanted was that box, jemmied open
to let years of lost words spill out –
bibble, fittle, tay, wum,
vowels ferrous as nails, consonants

you could lick the coal from.
I wanted to swallow them all: the pits,
railways, factories thunking and clanging
the night shift, the red brick
back-to-back you were born in.

I wanted to forge your voice
in my mouth, a blacksmith's furnace;
shout it from the roofs,
send your words, like pigeons,
fluttering for home.

Birmingham Roller

"We spent our lives down in the blackness…
those birds brought us up to the light."
(Jim Showell – *Tumbling Pigeons and the Black Country*)

Wench, yowm the colour of ower town:
concrete, steel, oily rainbow of the cut.

Ower streets am in yer wings,
ower factory chimdeys plumes on yer chest,

yer heart's the china ower owd girls dust
in their tranklement cabinets.

Bred to dazzlin in backyards by men
whose onds grew soft as feathers

just to touch you, cradle you from egg
through each jeth-defying tumble.

Little acrobat of the terraces,
we'm winged when we gaze at you

jimmucking the breeze, somersaulting through
the white breathed prayer of January

and rolling back up like a babby's yo-yo
caught by the open donny of the clouds.

Black Country – **Standard**

yowm – you are	*cut* – canal	*tranklement* – bits & bobs or ornaments
ond – hands	*jeth* – death	*jimmucking* – shaking
babby – little child		*donny* – hand

Sow

"Dainty footwear turns a young lady into an altogether
more beautiful creature…"
(*Etiquette for Ladies* – Eliza Sell)

Trottering down the oss road in me new hooves
I'm farmyardy sweet, fresh from the filth
of straw an' swill, the trembly-leg sniff
of the slaughter wagon. A guzzler, gilt.
Trollopy an' canting. Root yer tongue beneath
me frock an' gulp the brute stench of the sty.

I've stopped denying meself: nibbling
grateful as a pet on baby-leaves, afeared
of the glutton of belly an' rump. I've sunk
an when lads howd out opples on soft city palms
I guttle an' spit, for I need a mon
wi' a body like a trough of tumbly slop
to bury me snout in.

All them saft years of hiding at 'ome
then prancing like a pony for some sod to bridle
an' shove down the pit, shying away
from 'is dirty fists. All them nights,
me eyes rolling white in the dark when the sow I am
was squailin an' biting to gerrout.

Now no mon dare scupper me,
nor fancy-arse bints, for I've kicked the fence
an' I'm riling on me back in the muck,
out of me mind wi' grunting pleasure,
trotters pointing to the heavens like chimdey pots,
sticking V to the cockerel
prissy an' crowing on 'is high church spire.

oss road – street	*gilt* – sow	*canting* – cheeky or saucy
guttle – chew	*mon* – man	*saft* – foolish
squalin – squealing or crying		*bints* – derogatory slang for girls

Bilston Enamels

Open me up
and peep at er inside,
Iris, head bowed in the factory
of er mom's back room, painting a throstle
wi' a brush med of a single black badger's hair.
Allus summat romantic: turtley doves, Portmeirion,
This and the giver are thine forever. Fancy tranklements
for folk to hold the relics of their lives: an auburn curl,
a babby's fust milk tooth like a Victorian sea pearl,
a gold ring, ticket stub, pinch of snuff, a folded
cutting from the Birmingham Post
about that lad who tumbled
like a pigeon from
the roof.

fust – first   *tranklements* – ornaments

Tipton-On-Cut

Come wi' me, bab, wum to Tipton-on-Cut,
the real Little Venice, reisty and wild as the midden in August.
We'll glide along Telford's fabled waterways
on board *Summat in the Waerter* or *Our Wench of Brum*.
Or like Lady Godiva, we'll trot in on an oss
who's guttling clover at the edge of the bonk.
We'll goo straight to the sweet cabbage heart of 'local':
shout 'oiright' to blokes lugging spuds in their allotments,
yawning in the dark to call centres and factories;
we'll flirt wi' Romeos, grooming at *Tip'N'Cut*,
sunning emselves to creosote fences down the tan shop.
We'll blow a kiss to ower bostin native wenches:
owd uns, young uns, all dolled-up,
white as bingo-china or brown as the cut,
some wi' their babbies and some with their bargains,
some salwaar'd in blue-pop and cherryade silk.
Come, let's raise a toast to Aynuk in *The Fountain*
or *Noah's Ark* with its pairs of china dogs and brass osses.
We'll ate faggits and pays, batters, baltis,
crack ower molars on *Sanjay's Black Country Scratchings*
then goo three rounds, bare-knuckle, in the Jubilee Park
wi' a lad the spit of the Tipton Slasher,
whipping off 'is trackie top in the randan
wet with sweat the flavour of Banks's.
If we win, we'll give thanks at the Holy Fires Baptist,
the hallowed ground of the Tipton Ladies,
the mosque all gemmed up gold and fairylit;
pay ower respects, with the owd boys,
at the crumbling altar of the BDF Steelworks.
Love, we'll gather the finest gifts of the region:
an anchor, a cow pie, a tumbling pigeon,
that metal oss that prances by the railway crossing,

a wammel in every hue under the sun!
Then we'll nightowl away in knees-up splendour:
kaylieghed, singing *Oh Tiptonia*
as we lie on ower baltied bellies on the towpath
to sup the moon, like the head of a pint,
from ower cut.

cut – canal	*oss* – horse	*guttling* – chewing
Aynuk – traditional Black Country comedy character		*pays* – grey peas
Tipton Slasher – famous Tipton bareknuckle boxer		*Banks'* – Banks' Bitter
randan – fight	*wammel* – dog esp mongrel	*kayleighed* – drunk

Tranklements, donkey-bite, jack-squalor: Liz Berry on Dialect

"When I first began writing poems in Black Country dialect it was like digging up my own Staffordshire Hoard. The area where I'd grown up, too often mocked for its accent and dialect, turned out to be a field full of spectacular words, sounds and phrases. Everywhere I looked the stuff of poetry was glinting out of the muck. Tranklements, donkey-bite, jack-squalor... It was utterly irresistible.

I wondered how its richness had remained hidden from the wider world of literature for so long. I'd read, and loved, a great deal of beautiful poetry in other vernaculars, Scots in particular, but very little that used the vernacular of my home region. There were Black Country joke books, dictionaries, comic verse and even a Black Country version of the bible, but very little lyric poetry, poetry which used the dialect to sing about deeper things: love, families, place, loss. Why? Was it something to do with the region and accent's reputation perhaps? Like many dialects it has suffered over the years from being viewed as improper and inferior to standard forms of English. Even now, Black Country and neighbouring Birmingham voices continue to top polls as the least lovely in all the British Isles and it's rare to hear a Black Country voice on television or radio, except as a comic voice. Negatively associated with ignorance and lack of eloquence, it's hardly surprising that writers haven't felt able to bring it to the forefront of literature.

Yet so many people who I love and have loved have spoken the language of the Black Country that it seemed to me a great injustice that it should be so neglected. When my grandmother (a strong dialect speaker) died, I found myself thinking a lot about the place she and I lived in, about its communities, its history, its language. Too few people were celebrating our home and our voices and so it felt important that I should try.

To begin, I needed to tune my ears to the right frequency. I spent hours listening to dialect being spoken by friends, relatives and old men in the pubs with their wammels and pints of Banks' Bitter. I read the gospels in Black Country dialect – "God ud promised we wen Adam an Eve fust sinned thar a saivyer ud cum" – made my family groan with the *Black Country Joke Book* and was inspired by the lads whose local printing business had revived 'The Black Country Alphabet' – K is for Kaylied, T is for Tara-A-Bit... The language was thrilling: sometimes tough and muscular like clemgutted (thin and miserable looking) or ommered (hammered), other times soft and delicate as jeth (death) and mither (bother or annoy).

I started tentatively writing poems which included a few dialect words, testing the boundaries, before attempting to write in my own version of Black Country. I use the word 'version' because the exciting and liberating thing about vernacular writing is its fluidity. Oral language is impossible to pin down, it's a shapeshifting and constantly evolving creature, and so to write in a way that seeks to capture its spirit is to engage with that playfulness and willingness to make-new. I enjoyed mixing dialect and "standard" words together, experimenting with sound and meaning. I wove old, almost forgotten words in with new and invented words, wanting to carry them forward for a new generation of readers and speakers. Above all, I wanted the voices in the poems to feel alive and urgent and to let the thrill of the language lead me into new and unexpected places.

I found inspiration from other poets who used vernacular language. There's a rich and rebellious history of vernacular writing, of poets and novelists reclaiming the language of their communities as the language of literature. I devoured the wonderful *Faber Book of Vernacular Verse* edited by Tom Paulin (its introduction alone is magical) and read contemporary vernacular poetry from writers as varied as Kathleen Jamie, Daljit Nagra, John Agard, Kei Miller and Katrina Porteous. I read novels in vernacular – *Huckleberry Finn, God's Own Country* by Ross Raisin – and listened to music from groups like the wonderful Unthanks who use the vernacular of the North East in their songs. When vernacular writing works it makes everything seem zingy and alive, what Paulin lovingly describes as "the springy irreverent, chanting, quartzy, often tender and intimate, vernacular voice... a language impatient of print, an orality which seeks to fly through its authoritarian net". Although much of the language was old, indeed writing using dialect is in many ways an act of preservation, it felt fresh and different, subversive somehow. Vernacular writing is an inherently political act and is often used to challenge ideas of standardisation and authority. As the little sow in my vernacular poem 'Sow' sticks up her trotters to the cockerel on the spire, her language also sticks up its trotters to standard English and the ways it represents and misrepresents the bodies and voices of working-class women.

There were important choices to be made. How could the poems capture the dialect in a way that felt convincing and recognisable to local readers without shutting out those from other regions? How to create poems which felt alive and not museum pieces? I wanted the poems to be open to all. The best poets are able to write about places that are very particular to them – think of Frost or Thomas – but do so in a way that opens them up to others, or makes readers think about their own homes and voices. Many of us know what it's like to leave a place behind, or to be homesick, to love someone from somewhere, to long to go back and be the person you were. So I tried write about the Black Country using its vernacular, but for everyone. I gave a small glossary at the foot of each page in the book to make it easy for readers to understand and enjoy the new words. The question of phonetic spelling was a trickier one. Phonetic spelling can guide a reader to the correct pronunciation and give them a flavour of the accent but can be difficult and distracting to read. Through trial and error, I found a balance somewhere between the two, a few poems have elements of phonetic spelling mixed in with the standard whilst other poems are written entirely in the standard with only a word or two of dialect. It was a process of experimentation, constantly rewriting rules and being prepared to make mistakes.

The response to the poems and their use of Black Country dialect has been extraordinary and I've been so moved by it. What's apparent is that vernacular writing still generates great emotional response in readers. It's a challenging and surprising way of writing, even in today's Britain, alive with multiple voices and vernaculars. Readers long to read and hear voices which feel vivid and real to them, to be transported by reading, shown other worlds. And perhaps this is why vernacular writing continues to enchant, to move us in ways that standard English alone cannot. Just as we marvelled at the treasures dug up from a rainy Staffordshire field, thrilled to discover news of life from a hidden world, so we take pleasure in the rich hoards of language held within communities. When poets use dialect, they lift this language to the light, show us its force and its beauty, reveal what it has to tell us about old and new, belonging and leaving, wum and away."

Lisa Blower

Mr Briggs's Next-Door Neighbour

It comforts Beth to imagine them as snails. In their slowness, their indifference. One day they will just retreat into their shells and never come out. A last moment of logic, she thinks, and their days of captivity end. She smooths out the crossword on her lap and doodles a kiln aside of the clues; shivers.

"Bit parky today, granddad. You want me to fetch your cardigan?"

He wants to know if she's smuggled in his cigars.

"Not today, granddad. I didn't bring my purse."

Her mother watches her from the other side of the dayroom. To her, his disease is a parasite. It burrows into the bedrock of the soul. She finds herself willing him other illnesses to speed things up. On other days she wants to punch him. Remember my first steps? That first day at school when I clung onto the classroom door until my knuckles went white? Remember who you called shoeshine boy? You walked me only halfway down the aisle to him, dad, for me to come to my senses. Why can't you?

He'd tell her he was picking coal at six. Bookie's runner at eight and on the pot banks at fourteen. Moonlit in a chippy on a Friday and Saturday saving up the wages for a week in Rhyl and there she was standing behind a piece of glass. Then he'd lose the rhythm of remembering and ask her if she'd come to clean out the fryers.

"No dad. You sold the chippy after the fire, remember?"

In the evenings, Beth finds her mother googling unconventional medicines and finds *why doesn't he recognise me?* in the search engine. He's taken to calling her Mr Briggs' next-door neighbour, as if she is the title of a book. Beth thinks this is lovely.

"You keep pushing him to feel something like you're expecting a miracle," she says.

Beth is sixteen and wears glasses for farsightedness. She's always been able to see the bigger picture, Claire jokes, and hopes that Beth's recent coffees with a boy with intense eyes doesn't distract her. She's been predicted eye-wateringly high grades in her GCSE's and that is not always coffee on her breath that Claire smells.

Back in the dayroom, and Claire watches her father look at Beth like she's something he can't put his finger on. He asks her for the nearest bus stop.

"We can go find the bus stop granddad," Beth says. "It's not far."

He takes her hand. When she looks, there's a sweet in her palm. Blackcurrant and liquorice this time. Those Sunday afternoons they all spent listening to the charts. He has taken to sucking the sweets first so they stick to Beth's skin. She's come to like how her skin crisps dry with his saliva and obligingly puts the sweet in her mouth. Claire hates this part. It seems so unhygienic. She watches him lean across her daughter to get a better view of the crossword.

"It's lightnin' that," he says. "12 across." He watches Beth spell it and frowns. "Ar found 'im jed in that storm an' all, struck by lightnin' as he biked home. Week later, an' we're all in us black an' in front pew sits his owd missus mindin' a cat. White Siamese eet was, 'ead on a swivel, an' she goes an' dumps this cat on the coffin an' starts yellin' – 'on your 'eads is this! An' yer'll get nowt owt o' me!' Any road, there's no wake or send off or nuthin' an' everyone's stood outside chinnin' 'bout her nerve til me mother says, well this canna be right in God's eyes, an' next thing she's got me passin' round cake slices on rips o' kitchen roll save the crumbs on 'er carpet. An' ar see this tuther woman out corner o' me eye an' she beckons us over. So ar goes with a slice o' cake like, an' she's got this disease up 'er face – ar'd never seen the likes be eet, and she says, ar'm sorry fer yer loss duck, but your mother's got a lot answer for. An' she knows eet. An' next thing, me mother's got me and our Alb by scruffs of ar necks an' tellin' us gerroff up them fields an' tack that bloody cat with yer. She hated cats my mother. Said they were bad luck – only 'ad t' look one in the eye and she got a rash. An' there eet was in a bin bag all tied up."

Something in Claire snaps, like her body is made of elastic bands and she pings across the room to put both hands on her father's shoulders.

"*Cost spayk layk a Stokey?*"

The words take on a life of their own.

"*Cost kick a bo agen a wo an' ed it til' it bost? Spayk layk a Stokey. Ar spayk layk a Stokey. Arm not your goddamn next-door neighbour dad. Arm your daughter.*"

He puts up a hand and strikes. Beth shrieks. Tea has been spilled. Her hand scalded. Granddad shouts for the guards to take her away before he shoots.

Claire and Beth sit in Grace Downey's flour-coloured office on a simmering red sofa where they are offered more tea, handed tissues, a cold compress for Beth's hand.

"He hit me," Claire says. "He has never hit me."

Grace looks at Claire like she's interrupted her holiday and says, "with all due respect, this isn't about you."

Claire sits remembering how her father had entered the home so cheerfully and clutching his wedding photograph. Told her, "you don't need to come in. I'll send you a postcard." The day before, she'd been called from casualty to come and collect him. He couldn't remember why he was there just that there *were summat mitherin'*. Claire took him home and found six-months-worth of bus tickets making the same journey there and back to A&E, all laid out on the coffee table like he'd been trying to solve a crime.

This is not the first time Grace and Claire have locked horns, and Grace takes Claire's blame on the chin as she takes everyone's blame because the blame needs somewhere to land – a pile of blame that she bags up and puts to the back of her mind.

"We've just never seen him that *whole*," Beth says. "I can't even remember the last time I heard his proper voice."

"Fools die hard," Claire mutters. "And you've got your exams." She knows what Beth is thinking.

"But it triggered something." Beth believes in miracles. "Something came alive."

"He's my father Beth."

The words sound far unkinder than they are meant. Beth's own father has never wanted to know and Claire is usually so careful. Grace suggests that Claire takes a few days off from visiting. Spend some time remembering you, she says. Claire eventually agrees, though it upsets her more that her father won't know the difference between her being there or not.

At home, over a takeaway, Beth says, "I want to try again with another crossword. I have an idea."

Claire is worn out and feels covered in dust. "I'm powerless whatever yet the enemy all the same," she says. "Do what you like."

*

When Beth was little, she used to find the crosswords screwed up in the bin. Letters where they didn't fit and never finished. He spelled the words as he knew them. She says, "Morning granddad, you want eggs?" and points to 7 down.

"That'll be breakstuff," he says. "'E were as pig-'eaded as 'e were bald-'eaded. 'Ad us all thinkin' he were sum war veteran who deserved eet when 'is whole world were fly-tipped furnished. All smug, you'd think his Auntie came from Brighton, yet he'd look you up an' down as if yer were summat he might catch. Emergency red tie and fancy bloody westcott all gradeley, he'd be at our door of a morning askin' fer a glass of watter then 'ave his eye on yer furniture. We tried follow 'im once, see where he really lived but never took a key t' a single door. Me mother always knew when we'd let 'im in. Said she could smell 'im and check the mugs. Which one he drink outta? Where'd he bin sat? Stood there with the Jif. Fungus and fleas she called it. Yer dunna give the likes o' im an ounce of yer breath."

And then the sweet in her hand. Lemon sherbet today. Beth's smile fills the room.

"10 across granddad. *Tried to get a bite, admitting mum's flipping hungry.*"

"Bi 'appens that's *clemmed* shug," as if it were on the tip of his tongue. "An' they can tell me mother what they bloody like, I onna bothered. I know what 'appened an' I never stole nowt."

*

Beth starts to record her granddad's stories on her mobile phone then plays them back to Claire at the kitchen table. She tells her that she waited in his room today whilst they shaved him and cut his toenails.

"He keeps saying there's a hole in his ceiling," Beth said. "That someone's moving his stuff."

There is no hole, of course. Beth, standing on a chair, had run her hands across and down because she was once the little girl who believed everything he said. But she'd noticed the changes. A figurine had certainly been moved, two pictures swapped around, and his reading lamp had been given a brighter bulb. She'd asked, "Has anyone been to visit you, granddad?" Claire hears him reply on the recording: "Clean us on a lick an' a promise in 'ere an' they'd of 'ad me tooth an' all if I hadn't've neck eat dine an' pretended eet in me belly." And then her father showing Beth his lost tooth. He has it in his hand and is rolling it around like a marble.

"Always pocketful o' marbles as a nipper," he carries on. "Put 'em in me handkerchief once an' clouted a man hangin' arinde our backway. Frittened 'im t' death. Said he was lookin' for our mother an' he'd be back fer what she owed."

Then he tells Beth that there was a gold filling in that tooth but he gave it to Mr Briggs' next-door neighbour when she came to ask for his autograph.

"She'd bin tryin' get through on the phone," he says, before asking Beth if she's come for a bag of scraps. "I canna find no vinegar though duck, turned the place upside down."

Claire finds she has her hand on her chest and something solid in her throat.

"I thought you were going to stay away for a while and let me do this," Beth says.

Claire works hard to keep her voice straight. "I just want

him to do it for me," she says.

"It doesn't matter who he does it for," Beth replies. "It's not going to cure him so what if it's me or you? It's making a difference and that's what you wanted. He's eating like a horse and even watching the snooker. Listen!"

"I tell thee lass. I canst think the last time I ate a man of 'is oss and saddle an' all. I were that bosoned I thought I'd bost. Fassened meself in bed an' slept like a bloody babbie. Nurse comes in of a morning, 'orate Bill duck?' Seems ar bin a right slobberchops on me pillow an' asks me for me dreams. 'Bi happens I had no dreams,' ar says. 'None ar can remember any road.'"

He laughs like he used to laugh at a cracker joke. Claire puts down her fork and leaves the table.

*

A family gathering. Christmas eve. Beth plays a packed living room some of her granddad's stories from her mobile phone. Her mother is an only child as Beth is her only child, but there's a glut of cousins who keep them close.

"Ar let that cat go free," her granddad's voice, as if he's sat there with them. "Cheeky blighta only finds eets way back every night get fed. I 'id 'er in our back coal'ouse in the end black 'er up case me mother got wind an' she goes an' as two litters. Me an' our Alb sell the lot 'fore closing time an' call 'em silver linings. Starts us off thinkin'."

They laugh along with him.

"Play dumb an' yer given another rum," he says. "That's the lore of the rag 'n' bone. Help yerself t' a leg o'lamb when yer see eet."

Beth on the recording says, "Are you talking about you, granddad? I thought Uncle Alb did the scrap and you had the chippy?"

"Keep yer lawlessness orderly an' yer blather t' yerself," he says. "Dust as much as they want fer fingerprints but we never committed a single crime."

The room exchange glances that all end on Claire.

One cousin says, "Blimey. Is he tryin' confess?"

Another says, "He's tellin' us 'bout that fire at the chip shop back in '91. We did wonder, didn't we? We said eet weren't accidental the way eet went up."

"That packet 'e went an' made on eet from Tesco's an' all. Who'd 'ave thought blackened rubble were worth that much?"

"'E were what? Fifty-two when 'e retired? Makes yer wonder if 'e finished up work too early."

"They say worries keep yer sane."

"Ar they were a pair o' rum buggers were Bill an' Alb but she raised 'em with values did Dulcie."

"What yer on abart? No bugger were more o' werrit fer money than Dulcie Briggs. Ad-em running all-sorts keep a bloody roof over their heads. Y' know what she were like if she got sniff o' a pound, nowt doin' with values then, an' their favver were neither use nor ornament."

"Still, summat be said 'bout scrap 'n' chips when you think o' all that silverware in Dulcie's cabinet. Remember eet? Dust eet within an inch o' eets life and say eet were all won on the Bingo."

"Who's that bloke he's onna 'bout gettin' struck by lightnin'? What's that got do with owt?"

"Bi 'appens one o' Dulcie's gentlemen callers int it. Red 'at an' no knickers when she'd not need be proud."

Beth listens to the way they all speak – nothing bullied out of this lot. Kept themselves true – and realises that what we come to find out isn't always the poetry we expect.

They ask how her eggsams are going. She laughs and says, "Owright duck." One tells her she's very ambitious. Another says, "Nowt at these universities that a day's work wunna tell thee better." Beth listens to her mother put them right and the pressure in her mother's pride.

Later, Beth tells the outspoken cousin that her mother is grieving. The cousin apologises and asks who's died. Beth is kind enough to say, no-one you know, when they do because he's still alive.

*

31

It is New Year's Day. Beth takes in a balloon that says Happy 80th Birthday and a slice of Claire's Christmas cake. She ties the balloon to his armchair and tells him she's brought a new crossword, one that's a bit different and she hopes he doesn't get too muddled. He completes it within half an hour, and halfway through tells her that the problem with old grease is that eet goes up like a lightning bolt.

"I bloody minded them fryers alright," he said. "An' Alb wunna 'ave eet but we'd bin 'ad with that oil. Drained from someplace else an' passed off as brand new."

Beth thinks, if I could bottle that look on his face right now, because there he is.

She looks across the room and nods to her mother. She watches her granddad watch her mother walk towards him and, as he smells the bag of chips she carries with her, a light switch flicks on in the corner of his right eye. Beth offers her chair because she's just popping to the ladies. Then she watches them from around the corner of a slightly pulled curtain discuss the crossword. She wonders if her mother is explaining to him that her clever daughter had devised a crossword all spayke layk a Stokey. She wonders if the chip-shop fire did more than break his heart. Her granddad had never put his feet up in his life. She sees him take her mother's hand as if it's made of fine bone china and smiles as she watches her mother pop the chocolate lime he has stuck on her palm in her mouth and start to crunch. There were always her favourites. And his.

Later, Claire opens a bottle of fizz to celebrate. They swill out the champagne flutes and chink. He didn't say anything special, of course, but there was a moment, a blink-and-you'll-miss-it moment when he seemed like he knew he knew her and it'd come to him eventually.

"Yer cosna ever suck a sweet for more than a second," he'd said. "Guzzled yer milk darn an' all then blart with that much impatience we had t' start feedin' yer pobs get a good night's sleep outta yer."

And then, as quick as he'd come back, he was gone, back into his shell.

Rupinder Kaur

from Rooh

poetry
[poh-i-tree]
(ounn) art of rhythmical composition, written or spoken.

Not just English literature
nor the works of dead men.
Poetry is the art of women too.
Poetry is the art of black and brown too.
Poetry is living and breathing every day.
Poetry is the way my people live.
Poetry is the way my people pray...

Years of colonisation led us to bite our
own tongues
and forget that poetry runs in our blood.
Poetry is our liberation and poetry is our power.

****

waqt ne meri kalam phar lai
hath sade khali ho gaye
zuba sadi band ho gayi

Time has taken my pen away.
Our hands are empty,
our mouths are closed...

Everyone's mouths are closed. They don't speak, they don't talk
and no one is writing/

Perhaps I should eat a dictionary for breakfast
and a thesaurus for dinner. Perhaps then words will reappear.
And I will find the correct words inside me.
And I will be able to write about God like philosophers.

Maybe everyone should eat a dictionary for breakfast
and thesaurus for dinner.
Then everyone will realise the power of words.

Right now I see a river of words
dissolving into the west horizon...
The tide of time floats away.
My kalam comes back into my hands
and maybe it will come back into everyone's hands too.

****

Challa

Across oceans
        to my bedroom
entering my heart
the challa comes.

The challa starts searching
but finds my heart
        full of words
in displaced languages.

The challa doesn't fit
        but the challa sits

waking me up from a deep sleep
so that I see everything so differently
like I had been asleep for so long.

But instead of the future
it's like I have gone back in time
finding the words of my grandmother inside me
      finding words of a lost language inside me
speaking challa, challa.

Challa the word, meaning ring sometimes
meaning mad sometimes
and sometimes meaning someone, searching...

Challa.

The challa sits inside my heart perfectly
watching me fall in love,
watching me speak the language of my heart
so beautifully...

Challa.

****

I am the winds of Lahore
that my Nana Ji brought
across the border of Wagah.

I am the soil of Amritsar
where my father was born.

I am mixed with the air coming from Delhi
where my mother was born.

Who am I?
is a question I am yet to solve.
I am divided into names and culture.
I sit oceans away from Panjab
yet I write about Panjab.

I am somewhat British
yet more Panjabi.
I write in English
wishing I wrote more in Panjabi...

****

My grammar, my English
have never   been very good.

I've been learning   to balance languages
on the tip   of my tongue
since I was born.
While mixing   between my mother tongues
my English   often breaks
in places.
      I fall short   of English
and that's when   I remember my mother tongue.
But sometimes   all I have is English
and sometimes I only   have my mother tongue to cry in.

****

asa chal gaye pardas
te sadi boli rul di pai

we have gone abroad
and our Language is getting lost

****

I lost my mother
in pages of history,
in pages of literature.

36

I lost my mother

when I learnt a bc before ੳ ਅ ੲ
(oora aara eeri)

I lost my mother
in diluted pages of translations.

She can't be translated –
she is too pure.
            She is too pure.
But people never understood that
so I lost her.

And I lost her again
            while writing this...

****

            zuban ka nahi koi dharam
            yeh toh azaad hai
            yeh sarahado se paar hai

            The tongue has no religion.
                        It is free
            It is beyond borders

****

Ghalib's kitaab
sits on the doorstep of my mother's old home.
It travels across borders
and in through my window.
It awakens me from my sleep
so I read and read.

Shiv Kumar Batalvi's kitaab
dances by the River Ravi,
comes to the River Thames
and then a few miles further.
It too enters my room
through the open window.

Urdu and Panjabi
words spin around in my room
looking at each other
saying: *kya baath,*
asi rubaro – wow
we are face to face...

The words laugh at each other
thinking of the irony –
how they are brought together in England
and are translated,
how they meet on the lips of lovers
and how they merge into the ocean of language.
How funny to see
how some understand them better than others
and how some don't even want to know them.

Keats and Blake are watching
as Urdu and Panjabi meet
oceans away from their homes.
And Ghalib and Shiv meet
in the same century, at the same time
sitting together in my bookcase...

****

Aunty Ji from down the road
comes with her dosa diaries
mixing with the air coming from the south
to our Panjabi tarka house.

It's Diwali
and Aunty Amar comes and gives us a box of jalebis.
Lights are lit in every brown house on the road.

The house in front of us has cool white kids
who play in the road
while I play in my back garden.

We know it's Eid
when our next door neighbours
bring flashy cars to B21.
Mum wishes Eid Mubarak to them

The newlywed nineteen year-old Preeti
fresh from Panjab
comes and invites us to dinner.
mum says we'll see if we get time.

As I do my maths homework
mum reads Gurbani.

And now it's 3 pm.
I wanna watch *Bhaji on the Beach*
but mum tells me to get some onions
so I walk to the corner shop.
Finally, it's time to eat.
I eat my favourite rajma chawal...

And years later I still love my mum's rajma chawal
missing the ends of B21,
missing my old home on Wattville Road.

****

Steven Knight

"The story of *Peaky Blinders* is one that is very close to my heart. I know the characters so well now but, in a way, I let them speak themselves.

In this extract, the whole family are together and in a high pressure situation, confronted by the presence of old battlefield and social class enemies. Add lots of whiskey, champagne and beer and the results are as follows..."

From Peaky Blinders

1   <u>EXT. SNOWY FIELD – DAY 1</u>

A two seat horse carriage led by a black horse shoots through shot.

All we catch is that it's being driven by a soldier in a crimson uniform with a plumed hat. The passenger is a bride in a LIGHT PURPLE wedding dress, wearing a dark purple veil.

After the carriage has cleared we see a beautiful English country manor house, quilted in snow. Around and beyond are woods and snow covered fields. We couldn't be further from the darkness of Small Heath.

Caption: Arrow House, Warwick, England.
(Arrow House will be an important place throughout the series).

We join the carriage as the horse trots and the wind blows the bride's veil into her face, but still we don't see who she is. It could be May Carleton or it could be Grace Burgess. (Those who know will see that the bride is wearing the color of dress worn by widows). We ride with this odd pairing as they trot through the snow. A second caption fades up...

'January 7th 1924'

As the carriage climbs a gentle slope, it slows. At the top of the small hill is the chapel that belongs to the manor house. At the door we see four men in dark suits and heavy black overcoats standing guard.

The guards wear the slanted caps of the Peaky Blinders. One of them steps forward and takes the bridle of the horse. A breeze almost blows the veil away from the bride's face. The soldier (who we will learn is GENERAL CURRAN) steps down from the carriage and smiles at the bride...

GENERAL CURRAN   Make them wait.

The bride looks down, preparing for an ordeal. From inside the chapel we hear the wheeze of organ music...

2   INT. ARROW HOUSE, CHAPEL – DAY 1

The church is Norman and a treasure house of stone carved effigies and woven tapestries. However, it is small, and the stone window frames are rounded with age. Winter sunlight comes through the stained glass windows and the only other light comes from banks of candles in every dark place. It should look ancient and almost unreal. Then the faces emerge from the darkness.

We move up and down the aisle with a choir boy. He is handing out hymn sheets.

The church is divided by the aisle and by at least seven social classes. On the bride's side there are uniforms, braids and epaulettes which catch the candlelight. Mostly the bride's guests are men, old and young, and their uniforms are of the British army, some of the King's Irish Regiment. These men also wear their medals and their sashes. The women are dressed in sober dark clothes. There are four pretty young women in two groups of two who are dressed in twenties flapper finery.

As the choir boy hands his hymn sheets to them, we might notice a line of young cavalry officers in crimson uniform, similar to Curran's. Also a strikingly handsome man in his forties (ANTON KALEDIN) who is wearing a dark civilian suit (he will feature) and who is paying particular attention to the people across the aisle...

The choir boy returns back up the aisle handing hymn sheets to the Groom's family, who we quickly realise are the Shelbys and their tribe.

Progress to the front is progress through rank. JOHNNY DOGS is near the back with some Lees. Johnny has two wives (in the traditional manner) and they are either side of him. We can hear some of his kids playing outside.

ISIAH is standing with CHARLIE STRONG, CURLY and the other kin, who are all dressed in dark suits with their wives.

LIZZIE STARK is elegantly dressed and stands alone among the tribe. She checks her watch and checks the door. She's expecting someone. Next we find MICHAEL, immaculately dressed. He doesn't have the blinder hair cut and might pass for a young businessman or school teacher. The boy in front pulls a face at him and Michael pulls a face back...

The boy is KARL, Ada's son, who is now four. ADA is at his side. Then we pass, JOHN SHELBY and his wife ESME, who is holding a sleeping infant (JESSICA). FINN is beside Esme and looks every inch the Peaky soldier now.

While we've been away, ARTHUR SHELBY has taken a wife (LINDA). We don't yet know who she is as she takes her hymn sheet. We will learn she is a lapsed Quaker and is yet to come to terms with her new allegiances. She is good looking, at least ten years younger than Arthur and has an air of sobriety and authority.

Then we find POLLY who is reading the bible. She refuses a hymn sheet from the choir boy...

POLLY *(pointedly)*   Some of us know the words.

She then looks up to the effigy of Christ. We might guess she is not happy that this day has come about. *Polly doesn't realise it but across the aisle a handsome, rather academic man in his forties is peering at Polly.*

We will learn that this is RUBEN OLIVER. We will learn he is a minor portrait artist, a former soldier, and a man who apparently finds Polly fascinating. He looks from Polly to the statue of Christ then back again.

A head turns in the aisle in front and we see that it is Arthur, who is best man. He smiles at Linda (to give her heart) and then half turns to wink at Polly. He knows her mood and wants to tease. She glares at him. As Arthur turns back to the pulpit we come around with him. He is sitting beside TOMMY SHELBY. Tommy's suit is Savile Row and his features are calm. He looks to be the same man we left, though his watch chain is now gold rather than silver as he checks the time.

The bride, of course, is making them wait.

Tommy and Arthur wear white flowers where everyone else wears crimson. In this single shot we see Arthur and Tommy side by side, Polly, Ada, John, Finn and Michael behind them, all in candlelight. The family are gathered again.

Tommy turns to glance at his clan, then turns his gaze on the bride's side. He has no expression, but we sense contempt. Then Kaledin catches his eye. The two men stare at each other. Though we have no idea why, Tommy is deeply uneasy that this man is here.

Suddenly a side door opens and the vicar emerges in a black robe. It is JEREMIAH JESUS, an ordained Priest. He comes to the altar and prepares his bibles.

Many among the bride's family react with horror, or those that knew in advance react with disgust that a black man is presiding. Many among the groom's family hide smiles at their reaction. Then a blaze of white light.

The doors to the small church are thrown open and brilliant snow-light pours in. All heads turn. General Curran is framed in a hazy white light in the doorway. He removes his tall plumed hat.

John speaks loudly enough for his voice to cross the aisle...

JOHN   Here come the fucking cavalry. Late as
                              usual,

Heads turn sharply among the line of young Cavalry officers. (Ruben Oliver smiles). John angles his head at them and twirls his watch on his chain in a tight fast circle which says 'come and get it'. Trouble ahead.

Then the organ strikes up *'Here comes the bride'*. Everyone stands. Curran has his arm linked around the arm of the bride and is giving her away. Among the Shelby's all heads are turned to watch the bride approach except for Polly, who instead looks up without expression at the Virgin. She whispers to herself...

POLLY   Still only one virgin in *this room*.

Tommy and Polly's eyes meet. Tommy knows her feelings too. The bride is still covered by the veil, SO WE STILL HAVE NO IDEA WHO IT IS.

Both Grace and May had military connections. And there is no telling under the silk and lace. At last the bride arrives at the aisle. Arthur and Tommy move into position and Curran steps aside. Tommy takes her arm. We wait a moment. At last Tommy lifts the veil.

IT IS GRACE BURGESS.

Grace smiles nervously but Tommy has no expression. Finally he forces himself to smile too (his mood we will come to later). Jeremiah Jesus speaks to the congregation...

JEREMIAH JESUS   Dearly beloved. We are gathered here
                                      today to join together in holy matrimony
                                      Thomas Michael Shelby, and Grace
                                      Helen Burgess.

We hold the look between Tommy and Grace...

JEREMIAH JESUS (CONT'D) But first, at the groom's request on this
                                      cold day, we will sing.

A pause...

JEREMIAH JESUS (CONT'D) ...'In the Bleak Midwinter'.

3   **INT. ARROW HOUSE, NURSERY/EXT. CHURCH SEEN FROM THE HOUSE – DAY 1**

We hear the hymn being sung and view the church through a leaded upstairs window in Arrow House, which is a hundred yards away across the snowy lawn.

As we pull back and the hymn continues, we find a uniformed Maid (MARY) who is holding a crying baby, seventeen months old. We will learn the baby is CHARLES SHELBY, son of Tommy and Grace.

She takes the baby to the window that looks out on the church. Under the hymn we hear her whisper gently...

MARY   Mummy will be out soon. She's just there. Hush now...

The hymn swells as we move through an open door into a master bedroom. It is large with oak panels. There we see the bed neatly made with rose petals on the pillow. On the bedside table there is a photograph of Grace and Tommy standing on the bank of the East River in New York with the Statue of Liberty in the background.

There is also a formal posed photograph of Tommy, Grace and the baby.

As we move around the house we hear in voice-over, (under the hymn), snippets from the wedding...

JEREMIAH JESUS (OOV)   ...Do you Thomas Michael Shelby take Grace Helen Burgess to be your lawful wedded wife...

TOMMY (OOV)   I do.

The baby has stopped crying and has been put into the cot. Mary wipes shot and we follow her...

INT. ARROW HOUSE, STAIRCASE – DAY 1

We follow Mary as she trots down the sweeping spiral staircase and perhaps for the first time we get a sense of the size of this new house and the extent of Tommy's wealth. To confirm ownership there is a painted portrait of Grace on the wall of the staircase. As the hymn continues...

JEREMIAH JESUS (OOV)   ...do you, Grace Burgess, solemnly swear to love, honour and obey till death do you part?...

GRACE (OOV)   I do.

As Mary arrives at the ground floor, we see an army of maids and servants (some household, some caterers) working frantically to prepare a banquet hall which we glimpse through open double doors.

The hymn swells as Mary approaches a senior maid and whispers orders. The senior maid nods as she hurries on and we follow the maid into the main dining room where tables have been set in a rectangle with white tablecloths, flowers and bottles of wine...

JEREMIAH JESUS (OOV)   If any of you gathered here together have any just cause or impediment why Thomas and Grace should not be joined together in holy matrimony, speak now or forever hold your peace...

On the panelled wall there is an oil portrait of Tommy standing beside his horse, Grace's Secret. We come close to his face as Jeremiah speaks and during the consequent silence from the congregation. We come close to Tommy's piercing eyes in the painting. Perhaps we see a new arrogance there.

JEREMIAH JESUS (CONT'D) I now pronounce you, man and wife...

The hymn ends. Through a leaded window we glimpse the church doors opening and the congregation emerging...

A bouquet flies through the air. A group of Shelby and Lee girls fight for it in the snow and the fight is real. Beyond them we see the faces of the bride's family and a photographer, who is trying to set up among more Shelby and related children. Arthur, John and the boys have had enough and are smoking and passing round hip flasks near to the door of the church.

There is also a gathering of the young cavalry officers, all Sandhurst boys, who stare across the snow at Arthur and the Peakys. The Peaky boys stare back and we should feel the tension.

Ruben Oliver is making polite conversation but once again his eye is caught by Polly.

Colonel Anton Kaledin stands alone. He lights a Balkan cigarette from a silver cigarette case and has eyes only for Tommy. More of Kaledin later.

Off his look, we come close to Tommy and Grace as they are swirled around by family. There are kisses for Grace and hand shakes for Tommy. Johnny Dogs comes close and pumps his hand...

JOHNNY   Well done Tommy, welcome to hell.

He gestures at his two wives who are lighting cigarettes...

JOHNNY (CONT'D)   You've got the handsome one, make the
                          second one a cook.

ADA   You look beautiful.

GRACE   Yes but so cold...

Instantly Tommy turns and puts his big black overcoat over her shoulders. She glances at Tommy.

For the first time we sense a huge agenda. Tommy is furious. Grace is anxious as hell... Tommy takes Grace's arm and drifts past Arthur and hisses...

TOMMY   (softly) Arthur, get the bastards in the
                         house.

Grace almost winces. Tommy leads her toward the two seat
carriage that Grace arrived in. John is close to Arthur and Arthur
speaks softly...

ARTHUR   (softly) Going to be a long day Johnny boy.

A liveried servant goes to help Grace into the carriage but Tommy
takes her arm. He jumps up into the drivers seat and flicks the
reins sharply to send the carriage jolting away...

6   INT. ARROW HOUSE, GROUNDS, TWO SEAT
         CARRIAGE – DAY 1

Tommy steers the carriage along the curved path to the house
which detours away from the lines of guests, who are walking
directly for the door. The guests and the snow and the beauty of
the house frame Tommy and Grace. But Tommy is stonefaced.
Grace pulls the overcoat tight and prepares for an ordeal.

GRACE   Tommy...

TOMMY   There are cigarettes in my pocket.

Grace finds a pack in his overcoat and hands them to Tommy.

GRACE   I'm sorry. But I wrote it in black and white...

TOMMY   (interrupting) And matches.

Grace hands Tommy his matches and he wraps the reins around
his boot, Gypsy style, as he lights a cigarette. He looks across at all
the military men in the snow. Grace bites the bullet...

GRACE   Tommy, it was on all the invitations. No
                         uniforms and no medals to be worn.

TOMMY   And for a lark, they wear them. For a lark.

Tommy gees the horse. Grace tries to be clear.

GRACE   Some serving officers will not attend...

Tommy grinds the reins...

GRACE (CONT'D)   ...A social function in anything other
                         than regimental...

TOMMY   (interrupting again) We were Yeomen,
                         they're King's Irish. They know what
                         they're doing.

GRACE   They don't take orders from me.

TOMMY   My orders. My church, my house.

The horses have caught Tommy's mood and are scampering
through the snow. Tommy spits venom...

TOMMY (CONT'D)   (ploughing on) They come dressed for
                         war but I'll see to it they get peace.

He flicks the reins...

TOMMY (CONT'D)   *My* people listen to me.

Has Tommy become grand in our absence? The house, the portrait and
his manner suggest so. Or is it just this moment?

Tommy's anger is disproportionate but Grace appears to have
become accustomed to soothing his temper. Two boys trot
coloured ponies through the line of guests without a care and
gallop across the path of the carriage. Tommy yells...

TOMMY (CONT'D)   *Oi, chav!* Dismount and walk. No
                         racing, no betting today.

Grace almost winces at the echoing profanity as heads turn. The
boys instantly slip from their horses and grab their reins and walk.
The carriage is coming around in front of the huge house. Two
maids are waiting to help Grace disembark. As the carriage slows...

GRACE   Tommy, please. Let's just get this day
over with. Then it will be just you and
me and Charles.

Tommy tugs the reins hard and the horses rear a little. He jumps
down from the carriage and comes around to take Grace's hand.
The Shelbys and the military men are forming two distinct
honour guards at the double doors...

As Tommy takes Grace's hand he sees she is on the verge of tears.
At last Tommy softens. He helps her down. A much softer voice...

TOMMY   (softly) Grace I'm sorry.

As she steps down he pushes a lock of hair from her eyes.

TOMMY (CONT'D)   I wish it was just you and me in Gretna
Green.

Grace puts her hand to his face.

GRACE   Tommy, I know you hate parties and
people and talking about nothing, but
it's my wedding day so you'll bloody
well grin and bear it and stop looking at
your watch. You understand?

Tommy half smiles and looks away.

GRACE (CONT'D)   My people do as they're told too and as
of twenty minutes ago *you're* one of them.
So buck up soldier.

Tommy straightens his collar and bucks up. A burst of loud jazz.

7   **INT. ARROW HOUSE, DRAWING ROOM – DAY 1**

The jazz band from the Eden Club is playing traditional jazz.
They are all black and the music is deemed unsuitable or suitable
according to age, not class. Guests mill and drink champagne

served by maids in black and white. We hear snippets from the guests as we move around with a servant and a tray of drinks...

OFFICER 1   I warned you. Place is full of gypsies and blacks...

We drift on as we glimpse Tommy in conversation with Arthur through the crowd. A military man is glancing at him and informing two ladies softly...

OFFICER 2   ...Grace says he exports automobiles to the colonies...

LADY 1   (genuinely puzzled) So why did one of the cavalry boys refer to him as Al Capone?

In the background we can see Tommy's conversation with Arthur...

LADY 2   Aren't widows meant to wear black?

LADY 1   No, the convention is lilac or mauve.

We drift on and find Polly taking a cigarette from a cigarette box. As she puts it to her lips, a silver cigarette lighter snaps into life. Ruben Oliver is offering her a light. He speaks softly...

RUBEN   Question. Can you see me?

Polly reacts with puzzlement as she takes a light.

RUBEN (CONT'D)   The guests on the Bride's side of the aisle are looking straight through me. I wondered if I might have more luck with the Groom's people.

Polly smokes and looks around...

POLLY   I hear only a voice.

Ruben takes a cigarette too and lights it.

RUBEN   So I am a ghost. Who are you?...

Polly peers at him and offers her hand to shake...

POLLY	I'm a ghost too. Why are they ignoring you?
RUBEN	Oh they have their reasons. I heard a rumour about cocaine.

Polly reacts...

RUBEN (CONT'D)	The London train was abuzz with it.
POLLY	You want me to get you cocaine?
RUBEN	No, that isn't why I came to talk to you.
POLLY	Then why?
RUBEN	The way you looked at the effigy of Christ. I couldn't tell if you were angry with him or asking his forgiveness.

Polly becomes serious and looks away. Ruben takes out a business card and offers it (we glimpse the name 'Ruben Oliver' and 'Portraiture').

RUBEN (CONT'D)	I'm a painter. So expressions interest me.

Polly takes the card.

RUBEN (CONT'D)	I painted Grace's father in full dragoon colours. Grace took to me. Her family didn't.

She looks at Ruben and there is a connection. Just as it is about to develop, Finn arrives and bursts the bubble...

FINN	Pol? Tommy wants you.

Finn waits. She and Ruben are intrigued by each other but Polly turns to leave and puts the card into her pocket...

RUBEN	I'll find you.

His smile twinkles as Polly turns to follow Finn through the crowd to Tommy, who is giving a final instruction to Arthur. As Arthur leaves, Polly joins. Tommy is businesslike...

TOMMY   Arthur's rounding up the boys. Keep the
                         sherry flowing up here. Tell the Lee girls I've
                         counted the paintings. And be on your guard.

He looks around the room...

TOMMY (CONT'D)   Some of these people are not on the list.

Tommy departs through the crowd (in the distance we see Ruben watching the exchange) and we follow Tommy. He takes us past Charlie Strong who is deep in conversation with two pretty young 'debs'. The debs watch Tommy pass...

CHARLIE   His Grandad was a Prince. Came direct from
                         Egypt. On a camel. He bought his wife with
                         a racehorse and a diamond he found in a
                         salt mine when he was a slave.

The two young girls are rather puzzled. Arthur has arrived on his mission.

ARTHUR   Charlie. Tommy wants a meeting in the
                         kitchen...

Charlie nods and downs his drink. Arthur drifts on and we follow him. As we go, we hear the older of the two debs (CHARLOTTE MURRAY)...

CHARLOTTE   (to Charlie) Actually, we were told on the
                         train there would be cocaine.

Arthur approaches John, who is alone and swigging champagne...

ARTHUR   John. Tommy says the kitchen. Now.

John is glaring across the room at the group of six young cavalry officers in full dress uniform. Arthur follows his eyeline.

JOHN   I swear to God them fucking Cavalry boys
                        are asking for it.

ARTHUR   That's why Tommy wants to talk to us in
                        the kitchen.

John is seething as he finishes his whisky. Arthur goes to pass the
message to a couple of other Peaky boys and we follow a waiter
to Isiah who is talking to an elderly lady...

ISIAH   As well as exports, we do insurance.
                        Against accidents and poor health...

Charlotte, who asked for cocaine, comes by and taps Isiah's
shoulder. Isiah steps out of the conversation he is in...

CHARLOTTE   Sorry, but I was told to ask someone
                        young. Will there be cocaine?

Isiah puts his empty glass onto a table and smiles.

CHARLIE (CONT'D)

ISIAH   Sweetheart, I am young, equipped and
                        well informed, you chose your man wisely...

Isiah prepares to lead them away but Arthur breezes by...

ARTHUR   Isiah. Tommy says the kitchen.

Isiah hisses...

ISIAH   Arthur, these ladies want to play in the snow...

ARTHUR   (half repeating) No snow today. The
                        kitchen. Now.

Arthur walks down the corridor and further down we hear Lizzie Stark yelling at Michael...

LIZZIE   It was nothing to do with him! It's nothing to do with any of you!

Arthur reacts and prepares for an ordeal. A maid hurries by with a tray of drinks and Arthur grabs a bottle of whiskey as she passes...

Arthur arrives and Lizzie instantly turns on him...

LIZZIE (CONT'D)   Another fucking parish Parson.

ARTHUR   Michael. The kitchen. See you there.

Arthur swigs from the bottle and turns to depart fast...

LIZZIE   Arthur. You know why he didn't come don't you.

Arthur turns, knowing –

ARTHUR   Why who didn't come?

LIZZIE   My bloody man.

ARTHUR   (softly) You mean the WOP?

LIZZIE   There was a fire at his restaurant. Midnight last night.

ARTHUR   Michael, come on...

LIZZIE   And a smashed back window and a smell of petrol.

Michael grabs his cigarettes and matches...

MICHAEL   Lizzie, we tried to talk some sense into
                           you. We did checks on him. He's had five
                           names in six years. He's got connections
                           with the Naples boys...

She turns on Michael...

LIZZIE   What do you know about love?

Michael checks his look in the mirror...

LIZZIE (CONT'D)   ...about when lightning strikes...

Arthur takes another swig.

ARTHUR   So it was lightning, not petrol.

Michael turns to go. Lizzie's fury is of little concern...

MICHAEL   (casually) Arthur, I thought you'd stopped
                           the whisky.

ARTHUR   I'm having a couple to remind myself why
                           I don't drink it...

         Lizzie yells...

LIZZIE   You set fire to his restaurant to stop him
                           coming. You have no right to choose who I
                           step out with in my own time!

Michael turns on Lizzie...

MICHAEL   Lizzie, you now have an important
                           position in the company. And you got the
                           order the same as us.

Arthur pronounces (with some amusement, bottle raised)...

ARTHUR   Until further notice...

Arthur takes a final drink and adds with mock theatre...

ARTHUR (CONT'D)   ...no fraternising with foreigners.

Arthur and Michael head for the door and Lizzie yells...

LIZZIE   Yeah, well, you can tell Tommy from me
                     all the girls in the office think he's losing
                     his fucking mind.

They leave.

9   **INT. ARROW HOUSE, KITCHEN – DAY 1**

The kitchen is vast and busy with cooks preparing the wedding
feast. Tommy is patrolling the small ante room where the staff
usually eat their dinner. He is checking his gold watch, deep in
thought, a fat cigar in his hand and thick blue smoke swirling
around him. He looks like an angry devil (perhaps he is losing
his mind).

The kitchen is full Victorian with all the beautiful trappings.

The boys have all gathered. John, Isiah, Finn, Jeremiah, Charlie
and Curly and some new young faces who are cousins. Johnny
Dogs is there with some of the Lees. Arthur and Michael arrive
as Tommy checks his watch again.

ARTHUR   We got lost. Tommy, you should do a map.

JOHN   Yeah. I ended up pissing outside up a tree.

Tommy draws on his cigar and smoulders with anger. He controls
it but barely and, again, we should experience an angrier man
than before. We hear the clatter of the kitchen in the background
as he patrols...

TOMMY   Right. Today is my wedding day.

Immediately John interrupts...

JOHN   Yeah and you said there'd be no Paddy twill...

TOMMY   (instantly) Nevertheless....

Tommy raises his hand to shut down the topic.

TOMMY (CONT'D)   In spite of there being bad blood. I'll have
                        none of it on my carpet. For Grace's sake,
                        nothing will go wrong today. Those
                        bastards out there are her family...

He taps his cigar in the air (he's taking his anger out on them even
though it isn't their fault)...

TOMMY (CONT'D)   And if you fuckers do anything to embarrass
                        her, kin, cousins, your kids, your horses, you
                        do anything...

Isiah raises a hand.

ISIAH   Tommy, what about snow?

JOHN   (grinning) Their women are sports, I'll say
                        that...

TOMMY   There'll be no cocaine. No sport. No racing.
                        No sucking petrol out of their cars. You
                        give them no excuses to look down their
                        noses. And Charlie, stop spinning fucking
                        yarns about me...

CHARLIE   I'm trying to sell you to them Tom...

TOMMY   But the main thing is, you fuckers...

He taps the air again...

FINN (softly)   Why are you mad at *us* Tom?

TOMMY (ignoring)   ...in spite of the provocation from
                        the cavalry...

He walks along the line and gets his face into John's face, then Arthur, then Johnny, then Finn, then Isiah...

TOMMY (CONT'D)   No fighting, no fighting, no fighting.

A long pause. There is a disbelieving air around the room and even Tommy knows it's hopeless. After a moment Arthur raises his hand...

ARTHUR   Tommy. With respect. Can I make an alternative suggestion...

10   EXT. ARROW HOUSE, STABLE, COURTYARD – DUSK – DAY 1

A punch is landed on John's face.

A ring, of sorts, has been set up in the half lit courtyard near to the stables. A fire burns in a steel brazier and two barrels of beer have been set up in a stable shelf. It is just getting dark and the lights from the house twinkle on the snow in the distance. John, Isiah, Finn and some of the Lee boys are all stripped to the waist and the cavalry officers are stripped to the waist too. It's the Peaky Blinders Yeomanry versus the King's Irish Dragoons.

As we join, John is fighting one particular officer and the rest yell encouragement. The flames of the fire flicker and icicles melt. Some of our boys are cut and bloodied already and some of the cavalry boys are cut too from previous bouts. Finn is washing his cut mouth in the horse trough. A cavalry officer is crushing a handful of snow against an eye wound. Then we find Tommy at a respectable distance, presiding. General Curran joins him. After a moment...

CURRAN   Very sensible idea Mr Shelby. Clear the air away from the ladies.

TOMMY   I was more concerned about it being away from my furniture.

Tommy is dead pan. Curran wants to break the ice.

CURRAN   We are rather like Generals here, aren't
                          we. Watching our men do battle.

TOMMY   Oh, we're not far enough away from the
                          fighting to be Generals...

Curran is half amused but controls it. Tommy lights a cigarette.
In the ring there is a relay of fighters who replace each other as
they are knocked down in the tradition of Gypsy bare-knuckle
boxing. Curran and Tommy watch... John and the officer fight for
a while then John lands a blow and the officer goes down. The
rules of engagement become apparent...

JOHN   Soldier four down. Next!

The biggest of the officers steps up and the fallen soldier
is pulled clear. The next fight begins. Meanwhile, at the
edge of the firelight, Curran gets down to business...

CURRAN   You know Mr Shelby some of us only
                          agreed to come today to bless this union
                          because of your exemplary war record.

Tommy says nothing. John fights the big officer for a while but
he is already exhausted. The big guy lands a blow and John falls.

SOLDIER   Blinder three down! Next!

Isiah steps into the ring...

CURRAN   But as Grace's uncle, and a kind of father
                          to her for many years, I am still deeply
                          uneasy about the many stories of
                          corruption and violence...

Tommy immediately launches a fast and even response with
hardly a pause for breath....

TOMMY	I have very good contacts with the car makers of Birmingham. They tell me officials from the War Office, which you control, regularly accept bribes to commission certain factories to make armoured vehicles for the British army. I have no doubt you are aware of this practise. As an exporter to the Empire I also have contacts at Bombay docks where you were personally responsible for the execution of Congress party organisers who tried to block the unloading of military provisions. Ten men hung from cranes. A month ago.Please do not talk to me about being uneasy. Drink the wine and smile. That's what I'm doing.

Isiah has flown at the big guy with flailing fists. Men on both sides laugh as the fight gets messy. Isiah is a street fighter. The big guy lands a good blow and Isiah comes back at him and knees him in the balls...

OFFICERS	Foul!
ISIAH	Bollocks!
JOHNNY	No foul. Box on!

Meanwhile, Curran has been silenced by Tommy's comprehensive response. In the background Arthur is approaching, wearing a long overcoat. He is a silhouette against the lights of the house...

Isiah and the soldier circle each other. Curran at last turns to Tommy.

CURRAN	You speak very forcefully Mr Shelby.

A pause.

CURRAN (CONT'D)	And Grace tells me your concern for your family is absolute so I am giving you the benefit of the doubt.

TOMMY   I need no benefit and I don't care about
                         your doubt.

    Tommy turns.

TOMMY (CONT'D)   But Grace tells *me* you're the best horseman
                         she's ever known. Horses are good judges
                         I think.

A pause. Curran offers his hand. After a moment Tommy shakes
it. At that moment Arthur walks around them and into the ring.
He suddenly produces a shotgun from under his coat and fires
off both barrels in the air. All heads turn...

ARTHUR   Dinner is served.

Roy McFarlane

Tipton

Tipton, this tongue-tipping
double syllable of a word,
this Bermuda Triangle
between Brum and Wolves.
This *lost city* quintessentially
Black Country, God's belly button
of the Universe has got me.

I'm 10 and visiting the cousins,
the only black family in Princess Ends.
Streets wide enough to pass on gossip
and a horse in somebody's front garden.

I watched cousins as dark as the *cut,*
larger than life, colourful as the Caribbean,
speak another language.
Only laughter, sweets and pots of soup
translated us back to a common understanding.

Ow's ower kid their father would say
with vowels big and round as his obese body,
then he'd give me a sweet, slap me on my back
and laugh his way into the kitchen.
I asked my cousin *what did he say?*
Yam saft, she'd say gurgling,
everybody laughing like the locks at the back,
where water poured in and everybody rises,
whether you wanted or not,
a lock that levelled off once the father
left to go to the pub or to the steelworks.

40 years later I'm back
walking past the pie factory where they serve
soul nights on sawdust covered floors.

Industries put to an eternal sleep
turning into a commuter town, it
still draws on you, pulls on you.
Yam olright it's dem lot
that are causing de problems,
with syllables that jab and slash,
sentences like the Tipton Slasher
the bare knuckle verbosity of it.
And there's an *oss* everywhere,
in somebody's garden, along the street
and a metal *oss* frozen in time
by the railway station
and an anchor
on the side of the road.
Not all things are anchored
in time or in a living museum;
cultures flow, merge and make
their own journeys into front rooms
as I say to me *bab* bending over
I cor walk past ya without
putting me onds on ya and I know that

Tipton, this tongue-tipping
double syllable of a word,
this Bermuda Triangle
between Brum and Wolves.
This *lost city* quintessentially
Black Country, God's belly button
of the Universe has got me.

Where you from?

What do you mean?
Where my parents from,
my generation, genealogy, gene pool,
my family tree, my next of kin,
or simply going back to my roots?

Where you from?
Birmingham.

Why? Because we've been blessed
with all the colours God gave us,
our cocoa butter, caramel flavored,
milk chocolate, black coffee,
turmeric gold, brown spice,
black as a Dutch pot; flavours of the world.

Where you from?
Birmingham.

Why? Because we can speak other languages
as well as the Queen's English,
mix jawanna with Punjabi
and ooroyt with Gujarati
flow lyrical with patois from the Caribbean
sing my mother's tongue from the lands of our fathers.

Where you from?
Birmingham.
Where Spaghetti junction mixes with the Balti mile,
where carnivals bump with Irish celebrations,
where Chinese years begin and
German markets mark the ending.

Where Heavy Metal was forged
in the workshop of the world,
from the Gun Quarter to the Jewellery Quarter
and that's only half the story,
so I'll stop going around the Wrekin
and in a manner of speaking,
Birmingham is my home and it's where I'm from.

In the city of a hundred tongues

i.

The night comes early in the city —
maybe lost, maybe on the run
but it's here to stay, it kneels and prays,
nervous in the illumination of street lamps.
Arms outstretched a barefoot Rasta stands
outside Waterstones and in a city of a hundred tongues,
in the tumult of identities, even in the din of it all,
you can find amity in this beautiful city.

ii.

Dis barefoot Rasta walked into Central Station.
Dis Rasta is swapping the sands of Morant Bay
for the brown leaves crinkling under feet.
Dis Rasta is not the famous Mutabaruka.
Dis Rasta is sitting in a Café breaking wisdom
with a writer. Dis Rasta has been travelling
a long way. Dis Rasta is he fiction or truth?

iii.

Rasta eating apple and cinnamon muffin.
Rasta: If you were to die today, what would your children
                think of you?
Writer: That's interesting; really interesting; Jeez that's
                interesting.
Rasta: Notice, you have repeated yourself three times.
Writer: [Silent]
Rasta: Write that down. Don't think, just write.
A writer writes, and a barefoot Rasta is walking out the door.

iv.

Standing inside Waterstones,
in between the *Good Immigrant*
and *Why I'm No Longer Talking
to White People about Race,*
the writer watches the Barefoot Rasta
standing outside with his arms outstretched.

vi.

Remember dis Rasta is not Mutabaruka.
Dis Rasta straddles histories of the
colonised and the colonialist. Dis Rasta
will not be policing state borders but
will stand in the gap in the midnight hour.
Dis Rasta will be the voice of violence
of the violated, the silence at the dawn
of revolutions. Dis Rasta will cry tears.
Dis Rasta will be seen and not seen.
Dis Rasta will at times embalm your empathy.
Dis Rasta at times will fuck up your mind.
Dis Rasta will not be found on the BBC.
Dis Rasta will be getting into your head.
Dis Rasta will not be wearing dreads
but you won't have to chase him out of town.
Dis Rasta will not be standing on corners
but will be performing from the BT Tower.

vii.

With Waterstones behind him, arms outstretched
and barefoot, a Rasta sinks into a multitude of tongues
bouncing off the soft paletes of black skies
and if all a man or a woman brings with them
is their mother tongue, in a city of a hundred tongues
we should always make room for another one.

Emma Purshouse

Flamingos in Dudley Zoo

Special ay we? He starts again,
always mithering with questions.
Great being a flamingo ay it?
Always bletherin' on he is.
I like havin' feathers, doh yow?
No different when he was an egg.
Tap, tap, tappety tap. No peace
to be had. He stands on one leg,
What was it like in the owd days, nan?
Doh half remind me of his dad.
Ay got the heart to tell him
as how it's always been like this,
the pond by the gates, the faces,
the chair-lift soaring overhead,
us sky-watching, pale with envy.
*When I'm growed up I'll fly the nest
to Chile or the South of France.*
His enthusiasm's killing me.
Yow best talk proper, chick. I say,
*or yow wo get nowhere in this world
like me.* He squawks. So pink he is,
so pink. My wicked tongue holds back.
I shut my beak. I keep it zipped.
He doh know our wings am clipped.

mithering – pestering or worrying

blethering – to talk incessantly or to talk nonsense

Two sides of the cut

What the canal that runs behind the low-rise flats has to say for itself.

When my pleasant face
is showud

    doh say as how
    yow ay bin towud
    to stay off the shiny bits
    and keep aht the oss rowud.

    Some days it's all
    salt of the earth
    and butter wouldn't melt
    and chocolate crumb smiles.

    And on those days
    when the sun shines
    I'm gin clear
    I'm coots and moorhens
    I'm irises and lilies
    the suck of the carp
    the plash of the ledger
    the whirr of a line
    hire boaters' laughter
    a million lock miles
    from disaster.

I'm all about benevolence
hiding my malevolence.

But
    doh say as how
    yow ay bin towud
    to stay off the shiny bits
    an' keep aht the oss rowud.

And yes
some days I am
a Sunday school treat,
I'm dangled feet, cooling toes
Jack-bannocks caught in a net
and then it's so easy to forget

the dark side.

On good days
I'm all about the romance
the damselfly dance
and I give yow
courting couples
necking on the towpath
out for a giggle
out for a laugh
chappin' and wenchin'.

And some days
I'm happy to greet you
with a smile
and for a while
it's all
life's so sweet
and it's
50 tons of scaff
delivered safely to
Newhall Street.
And I'm running like clockwork.
Steer to the bread.
Steer to the cheese.

On days like these

I'm a calm lunch break

a walk	trip
a jog	slip
a bike ride	skid
an ice slide	crack
the breeze in	
the willow trees	Timber…crash

Shhhhhh.
    It's all about benevolence
    hiding the malevolence.

    Doh say as how
    yow ay bin towud
    to stay off the shiny bits
    an' keep aht the oss rowud

    And then there are
    those other days
    those cross-cratch
    snide-hatch, slash down
    stair rod, cat and dog,
    struggling sack,
    black as slack
    sort of days
    when I'm
    heart-stopping cold
    and I'm every poor soul
    whose life I've taken.

    From the navvies
    to the babbies
    I'm every wretch that's
    ever drownded on
    a stretch
    or dropped
    into a lock
    and on those days
    the opposite is true

I'm all about malevolence
and hiding the benevolence.

So

doh say as how
yow ay bin towud
to stay off the shiny bits
an' keep aht the oss rowud

On those days
I'm cries for help
I'm the unheard
lad from Lower Green
who liked his pop

Glug, glug,
                splosh.
I'm the yelp
of a drowning whelp
I'm the tears
of the woman
who took her own life
I'm the toddler overboard
boat disappearing
in the foggy night
one less hungry mouth to feed

I'm the Brades Bridge
boatman's hook
pulling bodies from the cut.

On those days

I'm fights over stolen water
I'm no better than I oughta
                be
I'm *Go on I dare ya*
half a crown in the hand
to egg you on.
Ooops footing gone.

On those days
I'm watching you
catch your chin
bash your teeth
and I'm there
at your side
whisperin'
Yow'm agooin' in.

And then
it's easy to forget
the lighter side.
Because
On those days I'm
all about malevolence
hiding my benevolence

So even when my pleasant face
is showud
doh say as how

yow ay bin towud
to stay off the shiny bits
an' keep aht the oss rowud.

No
doh say as how
yow ay bin towud
to stay off my shiny bits
an' keep aht the oss rowud.

Keep aht the oss rowud – a Black Country expression for wishing somebody to stay
safe, often used as a way of saying goodbye.

Stay off the shiny bits – an expression used by some narrowboaters to tell other
narrowboaters to stay safe when they leave the pub at night in the dark. The
shiny bits being the canal reflecting light from the moon and stars.

Vera considers life and the universe

I wuz areadin' this book, yuh know, on the universe and all that, an' I sez to him, I sez, *John, did yow know that 96% of the universe is missing? Missing?* he sez like he aye really listenin'. *Yes Missing. Doh yow find that a bit, yuh know, worrying like? Maybe, John, maybe we'm like the Jona Lewies of spairce.* He puts the pairper dahn then and he sez, *Yow what? Maybe,* I sez again, *We'm like the Jona Lewies of spairce. Yuh know, John, like we'm shut in the kitchen at the big spairce party and everythin', all the best bits am gooin' on in the rest of the plairce. Maybe in the bits we cor see, in all that dark matter and in all that dark energy, maybe that's where it all happens.* Then he starts humming 'Stop the Cavalry' and I sez, *No, John, that aye the song, that aye the song at all.* And he sez, *What's fuh dinna?* And I sez, *Chickin!* And that wuz as far as it got really for me and astro physics last Sunday, that was as far as it got.

Summat Extra

Ower Brian only sez to me this morning, "It's about time yow thought about retiring. Yow aye gerrin' any younger!" He's a cheeky dog.

Doh worry, Mrs Baggot. I saw yower face then. I told him straight, "No way, Bri, I'll keep gooin' til I drop. What I do, it's special!" He laughed then and said summat about the permin' solution havin' gone to my head and curled my brain. He might have a point. What do you think, Cheryl, eh?

"Special!" he said. "That bunch of owd biddies am special alright. There ain't ne'rn a one of 'em younger than eighty." He's right I suppose. Elsie Maybury was 102 last Tuesday. She bought a cake in for us and we cracked open the sherry. Day we, Cheryl? Pass us that brush off there would you, Mrs Kayhill?

Cheryl, check if Mrs Johnson wants a cuppa. Er will do of course, milky, two sugars.

Our Brian doh mean nothing with his banter. I might be a tu'penny, ha'penny hairdresser, a back-street beautician, but when my ladies come through that door like it's a hedge and they've opted to tackle it backwards there's work to be done. Every week some of 'em, every other most of 'em. Regular days, same times, windblown and tattered. We sort it out on our little conveyor belt.

"You alright under that dryer, Mrs Oakely?" Can't hear me, bless her but 'er's waving so that's fine.

As I was sayin', the conveyor belt… in they come, gown on, sit down, cup of tae, hair wash, hair towelled, rollers in – they almost know where to go themselves those rollers – then I put my ladies under the dryer with a magazine, ready for another cuppa, a bickie and a doze.

When they'm done, I tease out those curls, pimp that hair up so their soft pink scalps am almost hidden. It's all candyfloss. Halos of white hair. Like elderly angels they am, beautiful.

They come to that desk to pay, straight backed as though they can look the world in the eye again and then comes my favourite bit when they wordlessly drop a coin into my overall pocket like a secret. Surreptitiously, like they'm paying for summat extra, summat special. Which of course they are.

Then they leave with a chiffon scarf tied loosely over their bouffant hair. So loosely it almost floats. And if it's rainy, over the top of that a rain hat. Job done.

You off now, Mrs Buchannon? Tarra a bit. Oh look, er's left it behind. Mrs Buchannon, Mrs Buchannon! You've forgotten your stick again. Never mind, eh. Cheryl, there's a love, put it over there with the others that've been left. That's it, in the corner next to the walkin' frames.

Paul McDonald

Me Exhost's Bost:
Thoughts on Dialect and Humour

"I recall arriving on foot to join a group of local girls on Yew Tree Common in Walsall, circa 1977. Expecting to see me astride my trademark Yamaha Fizzy, they queried its absence. Their reaction to my reply taught me much about the comic potential of dialect. 'Me exhost's bost', I told them. 'His exhost's bost!', they hooted, between teary-eyed convulsions, 'His exhost's bost!'. Suddenly I was a comedian, and the humorous possibilities of non-standard English have been a part of my life ever since.

I inherited my accent and my predilection for buffoonery from my dad, who my girlfriends, I couldn't help but notice, found hilarious: they liked it when he called them 'chick', and liked it even more when he called me 'yampy'. If they were lucky he'd offer them a cuppa tay and a chaze cob.

I relished my accent as a youth: I could entertain by exaggerating it, but it also provided a handy mode of rebellion, particularly when employed against those intent on educating me. I hated school, and played perpetual cat and mouse games with Walsall's truant officer, or 'wagman'; I'd pronounce it 'wagmon', and consider myself the subversive Moriarty to his establishment Holmes. My dialect was a weapon against such forces, employed in celebration of anti-intellectualism. Dialect, like humour, can be a dissenting force, then, and I vividly recall how mine became thicker the moment someone suggested I think about A Levels. 'Ay?' I'd I reply, stunned by their saftness, '*Ayy?!*' This accompanied by some choice Anglo Saxon, and the word 'off'. I wor the A Levels type.

My Walsall dialect continued to serve me well through my wispy moustache years, and was the perfect complement to my early career as a saddlemaker: the leather factory of my late teens offered a soundtrack of earthy slang and clacking tack 'ommers. By earthy I mostly mean obscene. Here dialect provided not just comedy and dissent, but solidarity. Yow day spake differently on the shop floor, not if you wanted to be one of the lads (or wenches, who matched us in colloquial ribaldry). I drew on the comic spirit of this banter in the saddlery scenes of my first novel, *Surviving Sting* (2001), where characters like Big Horrible Ugly Ken, and the toupee wearing Wigtits, converse with tasteless abandon. I can still hear my workmates assuring me, charitably, that my first effort at a saddle would do for a 'boss-eyed 'oss with its yed on backerds'.

So dialect wasn't a problem for me in early adulthood either, moving as I did between the Sabre Leather Company and the less salubrious saloon bars in Walsall. As is often the case, however, education complicated things. By age twenty I'd developed an acute sense of my ignorance, and a determination to read every book in the world, starting with my girlfriend's Danielle Steele novels. I joined the Open University, and because no one from the Open University ever heard me speak, I was treated like an intellectual. That's the joy of correspondence courses if you've an accent like mine. This changed when I enrolled at Brum Poly in 1986, where they occasionally found my twang hilarious for all the wrong reasons. I was as well versed as anyone in pretentious terminology, but having gained my entry qualifications by post, I'd no clue how to pronounce it. I'll never forget the semi-stifled titters greeting my references to Dezcartes, and don't get me started on Naychay. It was here I became acutely aware that my dialect had connotations of dumbness: it meks yow sound thick in ways that ay always funny.

You can see this represented in much of the region's comic fiction. Note the merciless satire of Wolverhampton in Howard Jacobson's debut novel, *Coming From Behind* (1983), where Wolverhampton (aka Wrottersley) folk are described as 'dim witted', and their accent is cited as irrefutable proof of this from page one. Or Meera Syal's, *Anita and Me* (1996), where, by the end of the novel, Anita's Black Country slang represents ignorance of a reactionary kind for the protagonist, Meena. It's key to Meena's maturation that she should ditch her 'yard accent', and as an older, educated narrator she employs it mainly to convey how comically stupid she was as a child. Jacobson and Syal are both gifted humourists, and I've learned much as a writer from how they exploit dialect for comic effect. One of my favourite scenes in all literature, for instance, is when Syal has Meena praise a pop song to an assembled audience of parents and po-faced relatives: it's so good, they're told, she 'wants to shag its arse off'. Meena isn't thick, of course, except insofar as she emulates Anita's slang, but in order to prove it she must leave such colloquialisms behind, acknowledging their incompatibility with a successful future. What about those of us who wo leave them behind? Am we thick? Am I bone yeded because I've called buses buzzes since I was a babby? Surely my mastery of the *Daily Mirror* crossword implies otherwise?

We may not be thick, but we certainly sound it. There is something about the accent that suggests it, similar to the way blues music suggests misery. I can't imagine this is inherent in the Black Country phonemes themselves; rather, it is a cultural construction which I assume developed over time. We're often told that our dialect is a very old one, for instance, and I wonder to what degree *old* may have signified *outmoded* over the years? Outmoded people are a bit slow, right? When one community posits another as thick, it occasionally seems to have origins in language. I'm told Athenians take the piss out of Pontians because their language is linked with the past and perceived backwardness; Dutch people make jokes about Flemish-speaking Belgians for the same reason: their dialect sounds archaic, and they're deemed to be dumb by extension. So is this where our imagined dumbness originated: with a sense of our dialect as backward, a notion reinforced in popular culture so often that it now feels true? It's not true, obviously, but for the purposes of comedy I, like other comic writers, am happy to play along with the stereotype...

This perceived dumbness offers much comic mileage. Just as ugly things are funnier than beautiful things, so dumb is potentially funnier than smart. Certainly you're more likely to become the butt of a joke this way, just as Jacobson's 'dim witted' Wrottersley folk are the butt of his, and the immature Anita and Meena are the butt of Syal's. Some philosophers argue that laughter is born of superiority: 'Me exhost's bost' is funnier than 'My exhaust is broken', because it confirms my listeners' sense of superiority over me – the revelation of my inability to grasp the rudiments of grammar generates a frisson of pleasure as my inferiority, and their comparative eminence, is suddenly and thrillingly revealed. And here's me thinking those wenches were laughing because they fancied me...

Even when Black Country characters aren't dumb, their accent can remain so. Consider Barry Taylor from *Auf Wiedersehen, Pet* (1983-2004), or Gordon Grimley from *The Grimleys* (1999-2001). Both speak with heavy Black Country accents, but neither is by any means thick – in fact they are both intelligent and articulate people in their respective worlds: both speak eloquently, and both have a poetic and intellectual dimension to their personalities. We still laugh at them, but here comedy is created in a slightly different way. Along with superiority, another key feature of humour is incongruity, and the incongruity in Barry and Gordon is the mismatch between what they say, and how they say it. Their words suggest brains, but their accents denote dumbness, and it's this conflict that creates the humour. I've used similar incongruities in my own writing, putting Black Country phrases into the mouths of unlikely speakers for the sake of comedy: in my second novel, *Kiss Me Softly Amy Turtle* (2004), for instance, I depict Filipino nurses learning how to communicate with the relatives of Walsall hospital patients (as their tutor tells them, 'Yowre feyther is jed, means Your father is dead'); likewise in my third novel, *Do I Love You?* (2008), I created a wannabe gangster who mixes gangsta speak with yam yam, addressing people with the terms like, 'yow mutha'. Those scenes originate with real life observations, and incongruity underpins the humour in both.

Something else I learned from the likes of Jacobson and Syal is the importance of being sparing with the use of overt dialect. While I often narrate in the first person, my principal narrators tend to use Standard English in the main, or at least my version of the standard. There are several reasons for this: firstly, I think readers often struggle with protracted passages of dialect, and secondly, I'm not great at representing dialect phonetically on the page. Indeed, I'm rather tone deaf, and don't have a very good ear for accents at all. This is evidenced by the fact that, to my own ear, I have lost my Walsall accent over the years, and now speak with flawless Received Pronunciation. My students and colleagues at the University of Wolverhampton laugh out loud when I make this claim, so apparently it isn't true. I suppose this accounts for the fact that Americans think I'm Australian and Australians think I'm American.

After thirty five years learning and teaching in universities, I'm less likely to say, 'Me exhost's bost', but my accent stubbornly remains, even though I can't hear it much myself. I believe this registers in my narratives too, even when I'm not exaggerating it for comic effect. It exists at the deeper level of voice – the rhythms of Black Country speech, its phrasing conventions, its words and tropes, are written through me, and I couldn't shake myself free of them even if I wanted to. The great Birmingham poet, Roy Fisher, once said 'Birmingham is what I think with', and I could say the same about Walsall. It's what I speak with too, or rather, it speaks through me. I know my narrators speak 'my version' of Standard English because so many people tell me how much my narrators sound like me. They claim they can hear my voice in my fiction – this is a tad disconcerting given the often debauched and vulgar nature of my protagonists, but still. I like to think it betrays a laudable authorial integrity on my part, although it may just mean that I'm a crap writer. Either way, there doesn't seem to be much I can do about it, except make it work for me as best I can. I'd be yampy not to, as me feyther would say."

Yower Feyther is Jed

an extract from *Kiss Me Softly Amy Turtle* (2014)

The porter responsible for transporting me from my ward to the CAT Scan department was called Vernon, and he had a hacking cough. Several times we were forced to stop while he doubled up with a coughing fit. He needed to be careful when he coughed, he said, because he didn't want to aggravate his 'double rupture'.

At one point we passed a room in which a teaching session was in progress. Vernon paused for a coughing episode, so I was able to observe a dozen or so students being instructed by a guy wearing a collarless shirt and a leather waistcoat. The students looked to be from the Far East – principally, I'd say, the Philippines. The teacher would speak and the class repeated what he said.

Teacher: 'Ay means is not'.

Class: 'Ay means is not.'

Teacher: 'Day means did not'.

Class: 'Day means did not'.

Teacher: 'Yome means you are'.

Class: 'Yome means you are'.

And so it continued. I stared amazed as Vernon hacked his ring up behind me. When he finally composed himself, we moved on and I asked him about the class.

'Oh yeah,' he said, mopping his lips with his sleeve, 'he's teaching them Black Country English. It's to do with the recruitment crisis. They're having to go further and further afield to find nursing staff. They can all speak great English but they still don't have a clue what we're talking about in Walsall'.

'That figures', I said, wondering how long Vernon had to live and concluding probably a fortnight.

....

Following the scan I waited half an hour for Vernon to return. As he wheeled me back to my ward we passed a poster advertising an appeal for a new CAT scanner. So far they'd raised a grand and had another two hundred and forty nine to go. On the same noticeboard was an advert for BUPA which said: 'Freedom and Choice: It's Your Health'. Was someone from admin taking the piss, I wondered, or was the NHS losing faith in itself?

We took the same route back via the teaching room, and the guy with the collarless shirt was still doing his stuff.

Teacher: 'Now we're going to deal with phone calls from relatives.'

Class: 'Aah'.

Teacher: 'Ow is me feyther? Means How is my father?'

Class: 'Ow is me feyther?'

Teacher: 'Excellent. Now we respond as the situation dictates. So: Yower feyther is wuss, means Your father is worse'.

Class: 'Yower feyther is wuss'.

Teacher: 'Yower feyther is jed, means Your father is dead'.

Class: 'Yower feyther is jed'.

We'd passed the room before they got to 'Yower feyther is better', assuming they bothered to learn that scarcely uttered phrase.

'Dow Fuck Wi Me, Yow Mutha!'

an extract from *Do I Love You?* (2008)

I walked down the drive, switching on my mobile. It beeped immediately to tell me I had an answerphone message. Seven in fact, all from my mate, Dicey Price. I listened to the first, received 8.30 a.m.

'[Sound of Dicey panting] Trebbo. Things have gone mental. Blubber-T's looking for us. I saw him coming up Layton Road so I legged it down Petty Street and I think I gave him the slip, but watch out.'

The next was received at 8.34.

'[Speaking in a hissed, urgent whisper] Trebbo? Switch your phone on. He's still after me. I'm hiding behind some bins in Moss Street. What should I tell him if he . . . hang on . . . shit [sound of Dicey running].'

I was just about to check the next message when my phone began ringing in my hand. It was Dicey.

'Trebbo! BASTARDING HELL! Where are you? [I heard someone shout 'Yow tell im, bitch' at Dicey]. I'M TELLING HIM, Blubbs.'

'Where are you, Dice,' I asked, 'and what's going on?' But as soon as I turned into Kilbourn Road both of these questions were answered.

Dicey had clambered on to the roof of a bus shelter and Blubber-T, who is too enormous and lumbering to follow, was standing beneath. With his right hand he was pulling rubbish from a bin and slinging it at Dice: a crushed Fanta can followed by a half-empty bottle of Waggle Dance beer. With his left hand he was eating a Twirl. A queue of people waited for the bus, pretending to ignore the spectacle.

'Dow fuck wi me, yow mutha,' screamed Blubber-T, fragments of Twirl spraying from his lips. 'Just dow fuck wi me.'

Drugs had landed me in the shit.

Blubber-T is a nasty bastard. Worse, he's a gigantic nasty

bastard. Blubber-T isn't his real name, of course: it's his street name. His real name is Trevor. He doesn't have much going for him in many ways. For one thing he's named Trevor; for another he looks the way a fat person might look if that fat person had been raised by wolves. He's the same age as me, but where I'd spent my sixteen years sitting about watching telly, he spent his making contacts with every drug dealer in the Midlands. He's a pupil at Newbolt College, perhaps their most respected pupil – respected in the way only large ugly criminals can be. My ambition was to become more respected at *my* school through my association with him.

As everyone who's ever been to school knows, respect is important. Prior to my move into the drugs business I didn't have any. If I was lucky the cool kids called me Scrag-arse (because of my grunge look); if I was unlucky, they called me Wankrag (which also had to do with what one teacher called my 'courageous sartorial transgressions'.) To improve my status I'd been acquiring cream-of-the-crop skunk from Blubber-T and supplying my fellow sixth formers. Since then they'd adjusted their name-calling in line with the prices I charged. When at first I tried to make a profit on the transactions I was still Scrag-arse and Wankrag (although they tagged the term 'the Weedman' on the end). Wankrag-the-Weedman is a slight improvement but I was still unhappy. Then I began scaling down my profit and became Trebor, Slackerman, and Nirvana-Dude. Better. As soon as I started giving them the skunk for less than it cost me, I became Trebbo, Trebbs and the Beard. Better still. Selling skunk at a loss might not seem very entrepreneurial but, hey, money can't buy you cool. Two words: Richard Madeley. But how, you ask, how can I afford to make a loss on the skunk? Well, when I buy my drugs from Blubber-T, I don't use money.

Blubber-T is the world's biggest fan of gangsta porn. The majority of 'normal' people may not know what this is and, come to think of it, the majority of perverts might not either. I'm no expert myself but, from what I've seen, gangsta porn refers to a genre of films in which women are ordered about by blokes who wear too much jewellery. It does nothing for me personally, but I'm not a fat freak who yearns to be a gangster. The rumour is that Blubber-T wants to get into the porn business himself and uses the films as research material. You can find good gangsta porn on the internet but Blubbs doesn't own a computer because his dad is some kind of fascist who doesn't believe in them. This is where I came in. I had a top of the range desktop with state-of-the-art movie-burning software. I could ride the net like the Silver Surfer and, what's more, I could access porn pay sites with my dad's credit card details.

It had been working pretty well, until now. The problem was this: the Adult Verification System that allowed me to access the websites had cut me off because the old man's card was maxed out.

'Films,' went Blubber-T, 'I want me cowing films. Die vie die quality, yow said.' He fired a Minute Maid Orange can at Dicey and it ricocheted off the shelter, missing a bloke in the queue by a gnat's. The bloke was a weedy, trainspotter type who wisely kept his squeal-hole closed. He, like the rest of the queue, continued to pretend nothing was happening.

Blubber-T was pissed because he'd given me a bag full of skunk as an advance on a score of high-quality flicks that I hadn't yet delivered. I'd made the mistake of trying to palm him off with low-quality clips the porn sites offer as free samples. I thought they'd buy me time until I could get the credit card business sorted. They hadn't.

'Blubbs, dude,' I said, alerting the sixteen-year-old monster to my presence, 'is there a problem?'

Blubber-T turned on me. '*Yow!*' he thundered. 'Tremolo, yoam fucking wi me, bitch. Yow owe me some films, and cowing quick!' At this point the 404 to West Bromwich turned up and the people in the queue scrambled to board – even those who didn't even want to go to West Brom (which one can only assume is all of them).

'My name's Trebbo, Blubbs.'

'Just answer mi cowing question, bitch. And dow diss

me.' He popped the last of the Twirl into his mouth, tossed the wrapper over his shoulder, then added, 'Yow muthafucker.'

Another thing about Blubbs is that he can't seem to grasp that Walsall isn't South Central LA. Though this town is probably just as dangerous, Blubber-T's lingo – peppered as it is with 'bitches' and 'muthafuckers' – is out of place. Being a muthafucker in many parts of Walsall simply means you're sleeping with any girl over the age of fourteen. His speech is like a cross between Ali G and Noddy Holder. It would perhaps be less incongruous if he was black, but he doesn't have that going for him either. He is white; worse, he's white with acne. He's red and white: surely the least cool colour for complexions.

'Didn't you like the last collection, dude?' I asked.

'It ay the proper stuff, bitch, so dow try to fuck wi me.'

Blubber-T walked towards me. He was conspicuous in his orange tracksuit, mirrored Ray-Bans and what appeared to be five hundred quid's worth of gold. Had the latter been *real* gold he'd've been wearing five hundred grand's worth, but still the boy was bling. For reasons best known to himself he also sported a raccoon-skin hat.

The old man is always saying how teenagers are getting bigger these days and Blubber-T bears this out. He really is *massive*: six four and a bull-elephant's worth of kilos. Though, admittedly, most of this is lard, I still had to choose my words very carefully.

'Blubbs, the last disc was just to tide you over, dude. It was a goodwill gesture in lieu of the real thing. I'm having problems with my computer.'

'What cowing kind?'

'Nothing that can't be sorted, bro.' I noticed that Dicey had begun to ease himself down from the bus-shelter roof. The crack of his arse was showing above the waist band of his Wranglers.

'I want mi skunk back, bitch.'

Sadly this had long since been distributed around my school's key faces. I raised my hands and then pushed them slowly downwards in what I hoped was a calming gesture.

'The skunk's gone, dude,' I said, trying to keep my voice soft, level and, above all, respectful. This is the way you're supposed to address psychotics, terrorists and people with small cocks. Apparently they're less likely to go off on one.

Blubber-T punched me in the face.

The blow caught the bottom of my chin, snapping my head backwards.

'I want mi cowing films, two hundred bones worth of cowing skunk, or two hundred cowing bones, by tomorra, bitch!'

'Blubbs,' I groaned, praying that his rings hadn't scraped any of my goatee off, 'could you give us a week?'

'Denied,' he said, taking a four-finger Kit Kat from his tracksuit pocket.

I thought hard. 'It's my brother, dude, he's ill. He's dying. He's almost dead.'

'What's up wi im?'

'Deluvian skitters. It's touch and go, Blubbs.'

Blubber-T pondered this for a moment, his fat fingers working deftly on the wrapper of his chocolate. 'Kay,' he said at last, 'but,' he added, using a finger of Kit Kat for emphasis, 'yow'd berra not be fucking wi me.'

With that he sword-swallowed the Kit Kat finger and left. We watched him walk away, the tail of his raccoon-skin hat swinging in response to his lumbering swagger.

'What a mentalist,' went Dicey, as soon as Blubber-T was well out of earshot, 'although I guess he's a victim of the system and the illusory promise of capitalism.'

I straightened my beanie. 'How's my goatee looking?' I asked, offering Dicey my chin for inspection.

'Mental.'

Benjamin Zephaniah

The interview below took place in 2011 as part of the Aston West Midlands Speech and Society project. In it, Benjamin Zephaniah talks about how language is an integral part of his being, and the various influences the language of the places he has lived in have had upon his multicultural identity. From the Jamaica that was very real to him in his home in Handsworth, Birmingham, to the Birmingham that followed him to London, and his growing recognition of the responsibility he has to his community in providing them with a voice not only through his poetry, but also his media presence.

" Just a few times lately I've had a call from people who want me to kind of speak up on the behalf of Birmingham and the accent because of the way people put it down. The other day I had to have a head to head with Terry Christian on the radio on Radio 5 Live. It wasn't just about the accent, it was also about the culture in Birmingham. He was arguing that Manchester should be the second city, not Birmingham, but it's interesting why the Birmingham accent still carries that social stigma.

There was a time when I did an interview with a woman for a newspaper, *The Guardian,* I think. She asked me about Birmingham and the accent and everything and very jokingly I said: 'Have you ever made love to someone with a Birmingham accent?' and she said 'No', so I said 'Woah! You don't know what you are missing! You get a Brummie whispering in your ear! For the next few weeks (laughing), it was this kind of chatter with women saying 'I'm looking for a Brummie!'

I was born in Birmingham, in the Handsworth/Aston/ Lozells area. Having said that, I was actually born in Marston Green because my mom was a nurse and she wanted me to be born in a nice, posh part of Birmingham as it was seen then. But in those days, black people didn't wander over to that part of the city. To say that I was black and born in Marston Green was something else. But it was my mom's connections; she just felt she wanted me to be born there. But I grew up in the Handsworth/ Aston/Lozells area. My mom is from Jamaica and my dad was from Barbados, but Handsworth was very Jamaican at the time.

I was looking at an early film made of me by Channel 4. It was interesting because some of it was filmed in Birmingham and some of it was done in London. At that time I'd moved down to London but I sounded and looked a lot older than I am now (laughing) and sounded more Jamaican. That was the accent that we used, more than what was known as the Brummie one, although Jamaicans would hear the kind of Brummie touch to it.

When I was young, I guess I tried to be more Jamaican than Brummie, not so much because of being conscious of accent as such but in terms of the culture. Now Handsworth has Indians and Pakistanis and a very Sikh culture, but back then it was very Jamaican. You did Jamaican food, you'd hear Jamaican sound systems going on in the background, so it was like stepping into Jamaica itself. The rhythm and everything was very Jamaican. I don't just mean the rhythm of the language, but the rhythm of life was very Jamaican. I always tell a story you may well have heard before but it's absolutely true. My mother told me a relative was coming from Jamaica and I went into Handsworth Park. There's a part of the park that's quite high and I was only a kid at the time. I expected my uncle to come over the horizon because I thought that Jamaica was just next door. So I had this feeling that this was my world and when my parents said we come from Jamaica it was just like from there, not far away. I suppose when you're young you don't really know anything else because I didn't leave Handsworth.

When I was really young for some reason, my mother made me go to a school in Newtown even though we were living in Aston. Newtown was then very white working class with all white kids in the school. I hated it, I hated school. I didn't mind the area as such, but it was there I had my first proper racist attack. A kid just riding past on a push bike had a brick in his hand. He was riding fast and as he went past he just smacked my head and he called be a black bastard. I remember going home, blood pouring from my head saying to my mom – me and my mother laugh about this now – because I wasn't interested in why he called me black but I was asking 'Mom, what's a bastard?' (laughing) I couldn't understand what a bastard was. That was my big thing at the time: 'Mom, why has he called me a bastard?' My mother, being very Christian, didn't even want to say the word bastard. I didn't like the school very much because it was so very white, with very old-fashioned teachers. They were horrible to the white kids as well. I'm a twin and me and my sister were the only black kids in the class. When she (Mom) realised the school wasn't working for us, she took me out and sent me to a place called Deacon Avenue which is by the park in Witton. It was just so mixed, really mixed. And so being Jamaican was cool. There were some Indian kids there and a couple of Chinese. I don't really know the numbers but there seemed to be a lot of black kids there. So it was like slipping back into Jamaica, and then into my secondary school which again was very Jamaican. I go there now and it looks like an outpost of Asia (laughing). But when I was there it looked like Jamaica so speaking Jamaican was nothing. We felt we almost had to 'put on' an accent to speak to the teachers. Sometimes, I remember teachers would say 'You know, you can speak to me properly.'

At that age, I felt more Jamaican than anything else, and I was black before English. You know, I was a black kid before I was an English kid. I'm a bit of an unusual case because I started performing poetry in a very Jamaican accent. I was always doing it in the playground. It was easier than kiss chase! When I was about thirteen or fourteen and we really began to understand racism, performing in youth clubs and things like that, that's when people began to notice me and I started to call myself a poet. But then I got involved in a lot of crime, and was basically living in the underworld, living at night through crime. It's funny, the criminal world that I was involved in was very much multicultural.

The big change came for me was when I was trying to go straight and I decided I wanted to do something with my poetry. I'd played the places where a black person can play in Birmingham like youth clubs, and I thought I got to go to London. A couple of things happened when I went to London. One is I became more Brummie. For me, it was a defensive thing. People didn't like Birmingham. They would knock it: 'You come from up north, isn't that by Watford' or something like that. So I would become very defensive about Birmingham. It was really funny, sometimes to the point that I got in fights: 'Don't you say anything bad about my people!' And then *my* people were white people, well, Birmingham generally, and I kind of got used to going to Villa matches. I was a Villa fan by default, being born near the Villa. I guess it's like not knowing you're Asian until you move out of the Asian community and people start saying bad things about Asian people. I think that when black and Asian people have Birmingham accents, it's not as Jamaicans would say 'raw' as when you hear a real white Brummie speak. I actually love that accent, when they don't say 'baby' but 'babby.' When I went to London and started defending Birmingham, the other thing I started doing was sounding more English, toning down my accent. Actually, I didn't think of it as toning down my accent. I thought of it as 'I'm presenting a programme on Radio 4 and I want to be understood'.

I was doing an interview, I think it was after the Brixton riots, and I said something in a very Jamaican way. I was talking about the conditions of black people in London and I said something like:

Right now, I and I er suffer
I and I er feel the pain
And if somethin's not done
I go CHANT beyond Babylon
Deal with Babylon
Babylon burns now

Anybody who understands Jamaican talk knows that means we're suffering and we're going to rise up. Some newspaper man said I was actually inciting rioting and burning down buildings. I realised that when a white person speaks they're speaking for themselves, whereas I'm speaking on behalf of the community whether I like it or not. In those days, in the 70s and 80s, I used to do an interview and underneath it would say: 'Benjamin Zephaniah, black community leader.' I didn't tell them I was just speaking for me. I had this responsibility and unfortunately that's just the way it is. I think it's because black people have such a small voice in the media, so everytime I spoke it counts, it really mattered.

Then I started to do a lot on Channel 4. It's difficult to explain to young people now that Channel 4 at the time was the radical television station for the minorities. It was where to go if you didn't have a voice. I suppose my path is not really typical because it's so influenced by music and by me. As I said earlier, when I come to Birmingham I always feel like I'm coming home, it never changes. When I go on stage, when I start performing a poem, I go right back to Jamaica. I used to do a poem about *The Sun* newspaper:

I believe the blacks are BAD and the left is loony mad
And this GOD is mad and this government's the best we've
        ever HAD
Hence I read *The Sun.*

I'm playing a character here, but in my own poetic voice. As I said, back then black and Asian people didn't have a voice in the media, no black MPs, all the black people we heard from were from America. I wanted to speak for our community, because it's hard for a lot of younger people to understand. There were SUS (*stop under suspicion*) laws. If you were black or Asian it was so difficult to walk the streets at night, police would stop you and search you all the time. You know, I remember being stopped four times in one night. I was going from West London to East London and at the fourth time, I said to the police officer, I said: 'Ah, come on! I've been stopped four times tonight.'

The Handsworth riots, I could see coming. It's not really the same now. There are similarities between riots back then and those that happened a few years back, but there are a lot of things that were very different. When I see young Muslim boys stopped on the streets now, and being searched, it does remind me of being a young Rasta. Just being stopped because you're a Rasta, being stopped because you look like you've come from a particular religious denomination. When I see young Muslims being stopped and searched in London, sometimes I actually stop and just watch, just to make sure nothing bad is going on. But the issues are much different now. The reasons why they picked on the Rastas was because they thought they had weed. They thought they were rebels. It's funny, but the people who were closer to Muslim youth as they are now, back then were the Irish. I remember Irish kids in Birmingham going to evening classes to get rid of their Birmingham accent. Because you know (laughing) having a Birmingham accent… and getting rid of their Irish accents because having an Irish accent was, you know… I lost two friends in the Birmingham pub bombing. I remember after that how the Irish community were really picked on. It's a bit like, you've got people who hate Muslims because they read all about them in newspapers, but some people were like that with the Irish and some black people were like that as well.

Earlier, I said about going to London and starting to defend Birmingham. I began to hear the Brummie in myself. If I listen to a recording of myself, I go really Brummie towards the end. Oddly enough, I really don't like the way I sound. I like the way I sound in poetry, don't get me wrong, but when I'm talking I just think my accent now is so mixed up. It's not Brummie, not London. Sometimes I wish I was more one or the other, but this is me. My accent is a product of my upbringing. I've heard a lot of black and Asian people in London with real cockney accents, but I'm not sure if I've heard black people in Birmingham with the real, raw, Brummie accent. There are touches of it, but I almost think there's a difference between the Birmingham accent and the Brummie accent, because there's a white working class who, let's be honest, they're quite poor, who don't really get out much. They know their immediate little area. They don't go to London or Manchester, they don't go for holidays anymore, and if they do, they stick in a little group. They're not very cosmopolitan. That's not a criticism of them. I know lots of black people who are like that. But it doesn't broaden the accent, because everybody that they talk to sounds like them. The way we define class now, there's been so much change. You've got working class people now, who have reasonably good jobs and send their kids to really good schools. You hear their kids, and they sound posh, posher than them.

If I had a child now, would that child be seen as working class or middle class? Their father would be a writer, someone who's travelled the globe, who has a couple of properties. All those things that belong to the middle and upper classes. Having said that, if I had a child and they said 'I'm upper class', I'd say you bloody well aren't! There's a Bob Marley song called 'We and Them'. At the end of the day we do all this stuff, hang out with them at parties and whatever, but when it comes down to it, they know they're different from you. They'll let us come in so far. When wealthy kids' parents died, upper class kids would inherit money. Working class kids would be left with debt. That's changing, but for the most part is still true. If my mother or father died, I wouldn't inherit anything. As somebody who has mixed with all kinds of people in this world, including ones who own big stately homes, who go round in their land driving Range Rovers and have helicopters, wherever they are, their accents are the same. I've got a friend in Leicester, one in Scotland, and when you hear them, they sound like the Queen. That group of people, that class, have this accent, and the moment you let it slip, they know you're not one of them. It's the same with eating. Your fork must be used in a particular way. That class is very rigid, particularly about the way they speak, and they don't want to let just anyone in.

It could be that in sixty or seventy years, accents will barely exist. If the poor start going to university and moving around for work maybe we'll all sound the same. Black people will stick together but I think eventually it will change. When my sister went to Grammar School, it made the local papers in Birmingham, because the local black girl had achieved this. It was just not done. Now it wouldn't make the news. My point is that generally, real hard accents are harder to come by. You really have to go into a community to hear them. If you go into Birmingham Bull Ring, what you are hearing is a whole array of accents. I live in a place in Lincolnshire, and when I go into Boston you don't hear English. It's all white people but they're Polish, Latvian, Portuguese, Lithuanian, even a bit of Estonian. So you look at them and think, white people, white people, white people. People say, where's the Boston accent gone? It's almost gone. I made a programme about Boston, about the Lincolnshire accent. And so much of it was really important, was connected with the area. There's a word for the way girls walk and I can't remember it in Lincolnshire dialect, it's hardly used any more, but it refers to carrots – when you plant carrots and they grow a couple of legs. People that work the land would use words that related to the land to refer to people, but that's all gone now. A lot of words in Birmingham would come from the industrial, working in the factories, the foundries, but they've all gone now.

A friend of mine the other day, who lives in the States, said 'why is it that English people always going on about our accent? When they start to sing they have this kind of American twang.' I said, its rock music. Wherever you come from you tend to do that, because rock music came out of America. When they do hip hop, real hip hop, not grime which is British but hip hop, they tend to sound American. So when I do dub poetry, my regular poetry, the Jamaican accent just works with it really well. If you try and do this poetry it's like a rhythm that drops the tongue, brings a rhythm that shoots like a shot. This poetry is designed for ranting dance hall style, big mouth chanting. Now I can't do a proper English accent, but if you tried to do that in English... It's almost as if it was made for it, it draws people in and makes people listen. Sometimes, people come to my readings and I get the feeling that they're interested in what I'm saying because they just love to hear that rhythm and the Jamaican accent. But when I do my poetry, it's just natural for me to drop into my own accent. Although I was in Birmingham at the beginning, growing up in Handsworth, I thought it was Jamaica, so it's natural for me to drop back into my Jamaican accent when I'm doing poetry. I suppose there's not many of us, and even though when I'm doing my poetry, the Brummie comes out a lot too. **"**

John Mills

Them as wesh on Monday
have all th' week to dry

It wunna as if she lossocked about over th' weekend,
what with church and dinner an all that.
But Mondays, once she'd seen me sisters off schoo',
th' kitchen became a laundry.

Mar muther chased and twirled sheets
round the gas-fired cauldron 'er called The Machine.
I never thought 'er strong
but sheets, table clothes and the like

wus 'efted, mangled and hoisted
like sails in th' garden
or festooned on th' Sheila maid
like maritime signal flags beggin' fer pace.
A large pan throbbed on th' hob all day long
boylin' family's 'ankies inter submission.

The names of soap flakes seemed exotic.
Omo, Persil, Surf, Daz, with its blue whitener,
I cuddna fathom that ite
and thought wot as 'ow it must be
like them blue bags in crisps
or them other blue bags you did summat with
when yer got stung be a waspe.

It were soft, soapy, warm and reassurin',
just mey and mar muther.
All in contrast to the water
that streamed down the winders like sweat
and the sweat that streamed down 'er face like water.

Portrait of me dad

Being born two months premature
above a photographer's shop
wonna the best of starts.

I reckon after a quick slap on the back
his first breath was a lung full
of developer and fixative fumes.

Next his appendix exploded.
They had open him up quick and clean him out
as his innards were awash
with caustic digestive acids.
They cuddna give him penicillin
what as how the Curies haddna invented it yet.

Things, as they say, happen in threes
and his third was TB.
Their brass wouldna stretch as far as Switzerland
but made it as far as the back garden
where they put him in a three walled rotating shed.

Every hour or two four strong lads'd
turn the open side toward the sun.
How they knew where the sun was,
with all the smoke from the pot banks and steel works,
has got me flummoxed.
Perhaps they had some sort of dowsing rods
or a highly-toned instinct for finding it.

Mind you he had a telephone
so if he was cold, clemmed or dying he could ring
and his mum'd come out with a gansey or summat eat.

He were sent to a farm to convalesce
which means, *recover from getting better.*
He liked that but his father said,
Tinna the life fer a lad of mine
and sent him to the steel works.

He took to it like a pig at a tater
moving from rivet hotter to welder, cutter and burner.
He was strong, short and stocky like a Shetland pony
with huge hands like the hooves of a Clydesdale.

Never the sort of man to
put a gold knocker on a pig sty door
he called a spade a shovel
but always gently and with a smile.

Roderick Smith

Scenes from A Brummie Iliad

Adapted from Homer's Iliad

PART TWO
The Struggle for Patroclus's Corpse

CHORUS

It's late afternoon at the long black ships
and Achilles is stood with his hands on his hips
staring out across the plain
He can't make out what's going on
through the shimmer and the dust
Zeus however's up on Mount Ida –
He's got a grandstand view –
and he can't help interfering –
You know the way gods do

Hector's still buzzing from Patroclus's death
and he's chasin' Achilles's chariot
Fruitlessly as it turns out
what with Automedon being the driver
and the horses being immortal –
a wedding present to Peleus –
Achilles' dad –
From **Poseidon** –
Zeus's brother –
When he married grey-eyed **Thetis** –
The sea nymph –

But back on the plain beneath bright Ilium
Menelaus is stood over Patroclus's corpse –
A shaggy, red highland cow
protecting a first-born calf –

                    feet apart, head lowered
                    intending to defend it from the Trojan trophy hunters
                    who hesitate like desert dogs

                    But that kid is lingering out in front –
                    that pretty kid Euphorbus –
                    and he's fingering the spear
                    he's just now extracted from Patroclus's back

EUPHORBUS   My kill, Menelaus

CHORUS   He exaggerates

EUPHORBUS   Back off! I'm having his tackle

CHORUS   Lusting after Achilles's divine armour
                    and the kudos he'd accrue

EUPHORBUS   Unless you want some of this

CHORUS   The spear

EUPHORBUS   You've seen my work Atreides

CHORUS   The kid goes on to say

EUPHORBUS   I'll put a bloody hole in you. Get out the fucking way.

CHORUS   Red hair shivers and red mist descends
                    as Menelaus looks to heaven

MENELAUS   Panthus's son?

CHORUS   He says – a nod

MENELAUS   You're a bragging wanker just like your brother

who I killed this afternoon. I expect your mum and dad
are pleased he's coming home so soon. And his wife.
His pretty little wife. Don't inflate your status, mate.
Your brother was the same – "Hyperenor the Great"
my arse. Handy-bandy with a spear, but dead ...
by me ... be smart ... disappear.

CHORUS   Gorgeous Euphorbus ent gonna be cowed
and he vows to stick Menelaus's face
on display in pride of place
above his parents mantelpiece
with his armour as an objet d'art
analgesic for their stinging grief

He looses off his spike, full force
but it buckles on the boss
on Menelaus's shield
A quick prayer to **Zeus**
and the red-haired king of Sparta
rams his spear into Euphorbus's gullet
right where his rib-cage meets his neck
Oooah!

and down he goes, like feathers and lead
A sapling uprooted by a sudden gale
Bright blood stains the gold and silver
woven through his pony-tail

MENELAUS   I did say!

CHORUS   The Trojan dogs are thin on the ground
and they're getting thinner
as they leave the mountain lion
to finish off his dinner
Menelaus strips the corpse
freckled hands dancing

and blue eyes skinned
He'd have bin down the road and gone
if it worn't for **Apollo**

The mousegod is ubiquitous
busy filling Greeks with fear
and his Royal Brightness flashes
as he lands in Hector's ear
Riding him
Turning his head

APOLLO   Look! Look! Brave, beautiful Euphorbus, butchered by
Menelaus while you go
chasin' horses! Look!

CHORUS   Hector looks
and sees the boy's blood, squirting still
and the red-haired, red-handed Greek
busying himself over the body
A horrible sound comes from Hector's lips
so scary he could give the god of war some tips
Caught in a spotlight, Menelaus freezes
Patroclus's body on his back
a bag of booty dangling at his side –
Dilemma –
A glorious fight to certain death? –
(a star part in a poet's tale) –
Or –
An inglorious abandonment of Achilles' dearest love
to a dishonourable dismemberment
at the hands of the imminent Hector

The Greeks'll understand, he thinks
if he goes for backup now
so he dumps his load and legs it
He scans the dunes and growls
A reluctant lion retreating

110

                              from the dog pack's howls
                              He looks around for Ajax
                              He wants him on his squad
                              An oppo of old, he thinks that together
                              they might defeat a god
                              It don't take long to spot him
                              he's not a little man
                              and he leaps and yells profanities
                              to encourage his faltering band
                              freaked out by **Apollo's** fiddling

MENELAUS   Ajax! Come!

CHORUS   Calls the red-haired king
             and the colossal pair stride back into the fray
             They head towards the disputed prize
             scattering Trojans in their way

             Patroclus's body is already stripped
             And
             Just as
             Hector
             raises his sword
             to decapitate the corpse
             thinking to feed his torso to the dogs
             Ajax's massive shield is emphatically interposed
             and what do you know?
             suddenly
             facing a giant and a lion
             brave Hector's bottle goes

AJAX   Look at my face!

CHORUS   Goes Ajax
             And they do
             And they see his whole bloody fighting life

And they're fucking scared
Hector tells his flunkies to take the pilfered armour home
and off they scuttle
with the prize that'll score him glory points in Ilium

This ent no ordinary kit
Hephaestus's foundry turned it out
when Peleus –
Achilles' dad –
got hitched to the sea-nymph –
the divine **Thetis** ...
Achilles'mother, yes
Whoever wears it's got an edge
A godlike edge

The Trojan troops are from far and wide
and Hector needs them on his side
but the Lycians are deeply unimpressed
by his standing back
Young Glaucus sneers
at Hector's fears

GLAUCUS   Why don't you have a crack? As a leader you can't
                 hack it can you? I'm tekking my lot back to Lycia
                 where we belong. I ent forgot you left our Sarpedon
                 in the dirt. We could get his body back if we tek
                 this bag of bones for barter. But praps Ajax is the
                 better man. (PAUSE)

CHORUS   The air's as thick as hummus
                 as they stare each other out
                 The men
                 Ooah, the men!
                 Not men
                 Statues on a dusty plain
                 You can hear the sweat dripping on the sand
                 (PAUSE)

112

HECTOR   **Zeus** ...

CHORUS   Says Hector

HECTOR   will decide the day

CHORUS   And he turns away
            stops, looks back

HECTOR   Call me coward at sunset

CHORUS   And he recalls Achilles' armour to the front
            The men
            Ooah, the men!

            Close up on Ajax, akimbo
            frowning like a mentalist
            the bouncer you don't argue with
            even when you're pissed
            Menelaus has got his back
            solid as a sandstone cliff
            but doom is nibbling at the redhead's guts
            and he's weighing up the buts and ifs

            A high-wheeling, far-sighted buzzard
            looks back along the beach
            and sees brave Achilles peering
            his soul uneasy
            his searching eyes inadequate

            Hector strips off in the sun
            and puts the hero's armour on
            each articulated clasp
            each strap and buckle
            hugs Hector's swelling flesh
            in a seductive embrace

he feels a surge of vigour
a violent thrill
A blazing warrior, dressed to kill

Zeus the son of Cronus shakes his thunder head

ZEUS   Oh no. Oh deary me

CHORUS   He says

ZEUS   The poor kid doesn't know he's dead. You can't
            go stealing divine armour and expect to get away
            with it – you have to pay... Well you can have your
            glorious day but there ent no way you're going
            home to the healing hands of Andromache.

CHORUS   And he nods
            The way gods do when they mean it

            Hector's crowing like a cock
            There's war juice in his veins
            He's raising dust as he displays
            and dances on the plain
            He meks a vow that any boy
            who can take Great Ajax down
            and bring Patroclus to the gates of Troy
            will share his spoils and the victor's crown
            It's a lottery, where the losers die
            but they're young and
            'Here we go!' they cry
            The mugs

            Ajax is in the mood for severing
            Separating limbs and heads from lively young bodies
            and spraying the landscape with blood
            But even this grim harvester

doesn't like the odds
Menelaus is one step ahead
and he's got a special skill –
he ululates in shrill alarm
a war cry
A call to arms that can cut through stone
and be heard across the Dardanelles

The Greeks come running one by one –
swift Ajax, Oileus's son
known as Bjax to his mates
so as not to confuse him with Ajax the 'Great'
Idomeneus comes, Meriones 'the murderer'
and a stream of Achaeans, too many to list
arrive to assist the defence
and form a bristling barrier of spears
around Patroclus
A river of Trojans in flood pours down
and Hector surfs the bore
They crash against the Argive's scrum
with a comcomitant echoing roar

Oh, but it makes **Zeus** wince –
Patroclus had done him no harm in life
and it's in very poor taste, he thinks
to treat his carcass
in such an undignified way
He shrouds the body with a darkening fog
to take the shine off all these bright bobbing helmets
and help protect the corpse from further desecration

The Trojan wave knocks back the Greeks
but Ajax turns – a wild boar at bay
tossing dogs and goring humans
who venture in its way
Bad luck for Hippothous

who's thinking he's quids in –
He's lassoed Patroclus's ankle
and he's trying to reel him in
but his dreams of glory are truncated
when his face is relocated
by the wrong end of Ajax's spear –
Ooah!

his skull explodes
his brains come pouring down his nose
and he crashes to the to the ground and dies
He won't go home to his mum and dad
to reciprocate the love and tenderness
they showed him growing up in fertile Larisa

A glint
Ajax ducks
Hector's missile parts his hair
streaks through
Schedius – not so lucky – cops it
clavicle smashed, skewered lung
and out the other side
Phocia's best clatters down and dies

Ajax, wielding tools like a diner with a crab
attacks Phorcys – trips and flips him
finds the joint between his plates
inserts and prises, stabs and smashes
insides are outsides …
Phorcys digs his fingers in the dust
and death like dark molasses
floods his eyes

This shocking display dismays
brave Hector and his men
Not so brave, they crave the safety

of Bright Ilium on the plain
But the great god **Apollo**
Troy's best friend
has been in the dressing-up box again
He appears to Aeneas
Hector's number two
in the guise of an old retainer

APOLLO   It's unlikely sir, that we can win, without the god
          of gods – even though it has been known for
          mortal men to beat the odds. But *I* know **Zeus** is
          with us! He wants *us* to *win*! Still chicken?

CHORUS   Aeneas knows a god when he sees one

AENEAS   **Zeus** is *with* us!

CHORUS   He bellows, and by way of emphasis
          he disembowels Leiocritus

AJAX   Stand fast!

CHORUS   Great Ajax counter-calls
          And no-one's arguing
          Parents lose sons, sisters brothers, wives husbands
          all for standing fast
          Greeks and Trojans both, with shouted words
          like honour, glory, fate and death
          all say they'll stay and fight
          until their final breath
          They'd rather die in each others' arms
          than go back home and work their farms

          Achilles knows nowt of owt of this –
          beloved Patroclus alive
          and on his way, oh bliss –

back to the tent and a loving kiss
with tales of glory
His mum said – having **Zeus**'s ear –
that Patroclus wouldn't take Troy on his own
so Achilles likes to think that means
his boy is coming home
But mothers sometimes
and **Thetis** just the same
think to protect their sons
and eke out the truth

Shift focus to the dark centre
of an otherwise sunlit plain
the deadly work-out continues –
a nightmare gym programme
with a corpse as apparatus
Men on each side tug at a bit of Patroclus
as though they're stretching an animal hide
using their own sweat as a lubricant
A slippery and painful deadlock –
Lifeless bodies are held in suspension
with no room to fall

Menelaus catches Ajax's eye
They both know what has to be done
They need someone who can change the game
and Achilles is the only one
who can swing it
So the Spartan slips out from the dingy crush
and heads for the sunny dunes
He finds Antilochus, Nestor's son
who's as yet unstained by the news
of Patroclus's demise

MENELAUS   All is lost

CHORUS   Says Menelaus

MENELAUS   Tell him his boyfriend is dead

CHORUS   The shocked teenager strips off his armour
                and heads off back to the ships
                to plead with Achilles to come –
                to come and save them –
                His tears flow as he runs
                making tracks through the grime of battle

                Up on Mount Ida, **Zeus** is unsure
                about how to get what he wants
                Allowing Hector his glorious win
                while honouring Patroclus by delivering him
                into Achilles arms
                So he sends **Athena** to sort it out
                in her dazzling warlike glory –
                a terrible sight for mortal eyes
                so she thoughtfully adopts a disguise
                and dressed up as Phoenix, a wise old bird
                she accosts Menelaus and has a word

ATHENA   You'll never live it down you know –
/PHOENIX   with Achilles – if Patroclus becomes dog-food
                in the rubbish tips of Troy.

CHORUS   All innocence, Menelaus cries

MENELAUS   Oh Phoenix! If only **Athena** could hear my
        prayers. I know she would give me the
                strength I need. If only *she* was here.

CHORUS   Well of course Athena's thrilled to bits
                at being his go-to goddess

(These Olympians are strangely susceptible
to mortal flattery)
she preens a bit and grants his wish
and throws some added daring in
along with the persistance of a horsefly

His spirit is renewed
and in a murderous mood
The red-haired warrior takes a stance
and looses off a deadly lance
which fizzes through the heavy air
with a force so great
it enters and exits Podes's body
that's Hector's bezza mate, a cultured man
and great company, when he was alive
gone in an instant to glide through Hades dark halls
for ever
Ooooaah

They can't leave well alone these gods
always trying to fix the odds
Now **Apollo**'s at it –
bending Hector's ear again
this time disguised as Phaenops
one of his foreign fighting men

APOLLO/   Shake your feathers mate
PHAENOPS

CHORUS   He says

APOLLO/   You can't let him get away with that! No-ones gonna
PHAENOPS   tek you serious if you don't deck the twat. Podes
                 fought for love of you and deserves to be avenged
                 – ain scared of a ginga are ya?

CHORUS	Hector, revelling in the fight
	sees black and through his grief turns back
	to deliver his revenge
	his divine bronze armour gleaming
	Just then **Zeus** decides to stick his mighty oar in
	and the sky splits wide with crackles and crashes
	in an incandescent display
	The god of storms has got an Aegis
	which he saves for a rainy day
	And he's shaking it now –
	his massive thunder shield
	fringed with snakes –
	and from its dark centre
	a twining brilliant light
	curls and dances about the plain
	To signify Troy's triumph
	and the Greeks' continuing pain
	Ajax the Great is well aware
	of the desperate straits they're in
	and he calls to Menelaus
AJAX	We're gonna have to pack it in. I can't see fuck all
	through this pissing fog .
CHORUS	He cries out to **Zeus** to give them a break
	at least let them die in the light
	A gesture from the god of clouds
	and the holiday sun breaks through
	and illuminates the whole bloody landscape –
	Zeus can be a compassionate listener at times
	The erstwhile husband of Helen of Troy
	The flame-headed Menelaus
	knows that it's now, or never again

will Achilles set eyes on the best of men
He gathers his posse for a last hooray
determined that no-one will stand in the way
of his self-appointed task
Ajax and Bjax go in hard
and manage to win Menelaus the yard he needs
to nip in and shoulder the guts

And this is how it goes
It don't matter how the Trojans howl and harry them
They drag and carry the mutilated remains
of a man who was once pretty and kind
back to the black ships they'd left behind
an age, but not so long ago

Achilles walks like a cat in patterns
he's digging a trench with his feet
He knows deep down that it's all gone to cock
and he talks to his breaking heart's beat

ACHILLES I told him. You heard me, I couldn't be plainer:
'Chase them. Come back. Leave Hector to me'.
Fuck, it hurts. Tell me it ent true!

CHORUS But it is, and he knows it, and Antilochus comes
smeared with war dust and tears
He manages to blub out the word
'Patroclus'
And the world comes crashing up
to meet Achilles' beautiful face

There's no sense and no feeling *(clap)*
and you can't look away *(clap)*
as the great man tries to become one with the dirt *(clap)*
he smears and grinds the muck into his flesh *(clap)*
into his mouth *(clap)*

122

and his hair *(clap)*
which he tears out in hanks *(clap)*
to drown out the pain of his loss and his guilt *(clap)*

ACHILLES   Patroclus. Oh Patroclus!

CHORUS   Antilochus grabs Achilles' hands
to stop him reaching for a knife
He's crying like a babby
as he tries to preserve the life
of the reluctant warrior
Zoom out
and we can see the trigonometry of grief
gouged in the ground
by these weeping, struggling men
Joined now by women
Oooah, the women!
Not women
trophies snatched from their homes –
by Achilles and Patroclus –
their men slaughtered
as is customary –
But still
Touched to the core by this display
they encircle the men in the age old way
they beat their breasts and they keen and they cry
they stamp their feet with their eyes on the sky
The women
Oooah, the women!

Achilles tips back his begrimed face
and lets out a roar which can be heard
by a shepherd in the Caucasus.

R. M. Francis

Burning Tongues

We ay from brumajum
weem in the borderless
pits – black be day
red be night. Where baby
rhymes with Rabbie – that old
bard who kept the burn
in his tongue.
That burn connects, it burns
like our old forges burned –
burning trade and toil and song
and burning a brand
that yow know and yow know –
burns like Saxon shamans
who's embers were stamped
and pissed on by ministers
of education immersed in
double spayke –
thass why weem taught
to hayte those four letter words
like fuck and cunt.
Those words burn and words
that burn sit, like us,
in borderless pits, ready,
with Blakean bows, to fight
shot to shot – to burn back
with our vernacular,
thass why when my Auntie
sez *yow doh spayke proper* 'er's
playing 'er part in burning.

Sleepin' beasts

Skies mirror coal seams and slate of cinder smoke –
tethers grey birds to its oil slick,
cloaks wenches' washing lines,
hanging out failed whites
for blokes on the box
who doh know how to clear
the cloud in their eyes.

Down on The Wrenner land is littered –
winds clip used cans through estates,
passed scorched out sofas weedy teens
use to toll the day.
This land –
nesting tumour in a cold parish.

Iss like our Tim keeps cantin':
weem cut from 'ere in all iss umber,
like the cut was cut from clay.
We ay nature's sons,
just med of it, someway.
'Cause weem cut that way,
weem cut away.

Down on The Wrenner air is soiled
with unwashed pets, cigarettes,
dried booze, pizza crust breath.
This air –
pricked silica leak of rotting cells.

Tim treds the towpath to 'is ESA review,
over grit and sand 'e used to alchemy to glass
but now just plays a part
in weathering muck.

They doh know
wass under theya –
our earth's rotten
with trilobites.
Weem stompin' on sleepin' beasts.

'E's took 'is eggs to a fine market, ay' 'e?

'E's took 'is eggs to a fine market, ay' 'e?
Thass 'ow it started as we all drapped cork-legged.
'E was bostin' as a bab,
bought me suck on our run owem,
lamped that lommock Baggins
who was big as a Bonk 'oss.
'E's took 'is eggs to a fine market, ay' 'e?

The estate closed when the Patent Shaft was pulled,
Soaked 'is severance baked on Batham's,
'is wench left after that.

Grinding jaws and
chewed down nails and
archives of old magazines,
the same old clothes and
stinky shoes and
the way 'e looked like 'e wanted to say *'ow do*,
but quickly turned away.

But 'e was always ivverin'
and ovverin' by the gates,
while we was busy mekin' chains
and thinkin' of ha'p'orth dates,
'E took 'is eggs and went werritin',
blartin' like a gleed under the door,
while we were aytin' Tetnul Dick
and starin' at the floor.

'E's took 'is eggs to a fine market
and we all drapped cork-legged
after that cork-winder 'e gid 'im.

Julie Walters

The interview below took place in 2011 as part of the Aston West Midlands Speech and Society project. In it, Julie Walters talks about how her upbringing and subsequent career have impacted upon the way she speaks.

" I don't know whether people can distinguish my accent. A lot of people think it's Liverpudlian, probably because of *Educating Rita* and *The Boys' from the Black Stuff,* and other things I did early in my career that are quite well known. I started in Liverpool so a lot of people say 'Oh, you're from Birmingham, bloody hell!' They don't know about The Black Country, they don't know that it's a Black Country accent. I'm not sure either how much of my accent is Black Country and how much Birmingham because we lived so close, on the borders of both. So I'm not sure how you'd know, and when you hear about what Black Country accents were like, ours didn't bear so much of a relationship to it. But why have I still got the accent? If I still lived there I'd certainly have more of an accent than I've got now. Probably about twenty years before I came into the acting business it probably wouldn't have been good to have a regional accent, but when I came into it I was very lucky, in that 'kitchen sink' drama had happened, and grammar school education had happened, so it was actually a help. It was much more trendy to be working class if you like, than it was to be middle class. Places like The Everyman welcomed that. The Everyman theatre in Liverpool, where I first started, welcomed that.

In theatre, we were all virtually from working class backgrounds more or less, not all of us but most of us were. Also I didn't want to go away from my roots. That felt offensive to me, to try to get rid of the accent and speak the standard, although at drama school we did have standard English classes, but there was *no way* that was going to be my life. My mother had tried, speaking like this, she said (mimicking an Irish accent): 'Oh no, you must speak nicely because that's how you get on.' My father had a Birmingham accent and it felt wrong. At my *awful* preparatory school where we had elocution, that really put me right off and there's no way I was going to do that. It was a private school, and my mother thought, old-fashioned thinking, I think she thought this was going to make me into a lady so therefore I would marry a doctor or someone of that ilk. I wasn't going to do it off my own back, and she still hasn't got used to that. Grammar school education had only just started, and working-class women weren't going out and having careers then, not really, not like when they were in the sixties. It all changed then, but she was doing what she thought best sending me to that school but it turned out to be horrific for me. That's why I still have my accent, I've never made any effort to get rid of it, but I haven't done what some people try to do and keep it either. I've let it be what it is, and this is how it's turned out. But as soon as I go home, of course I start, or as soon as I'm with my sister-in-law I start sort of speaking much more like that because I can't help it. You relax into something you knew as a child.

I was asked to play *Educating Rita,* and the director said look, if you want to do it Birmingham you can but it just didn't fit, none of it fitted the sound of Brummie. It wasn't really funny, because it's a different humour, Liverpool, it has a completely different humour. It just wasn't funny in Birmingham, it sounded depressing. I'm not saying Birmingham isn't funny but not in those lines, they were written for a Liverpool head, so you'd have to write it with a Birmingham head. Liverpool's a very different place, with its Irish influence and everything. I'm amazed there aren't more comedians from Birmingham, I mean Liverpool is completely full of them, nearly everyone's a bloody comedian in Liverpool. When people parody Birmingham, you know you hear actor Timothy Spall who does Birmingham a lot, but it's always a little bit depressed, negative. I think there is a negative aspect to it. I don't know, it's the perception people have got. I don't know what you do about it. I mean, *Crossroads* didn't probably help, because it was a terrible, dull programme.

It never occurred to me to change my accent because of my upbringing. I saw snobbery in that even as a child, and I thought it was saying 'We aren't good enough, you're not good enough the way you are', and that's a terrible message to give a child. My accent has never held me back, I feel it helped. People like it in the business, rather than dislike it. As I said, working class drama was really the thing, so it was perfect for me, and a lot of people didn't know whether I was Liverpudlian or Birmingham anyway, so I'd get offered all of the Northern stuff, it was all lumped in together. Later, I was established anyway, and I have played other parts in a more standard accent.

Mark Williams, who played my husband in *Harry Potter*, he's from Bromsgrove, and got a proper Midlands accent. He's talked about how prejudiced people are towards it. He went to Oxford University and is really bright. He met some producer at the BBC at some BAFTA awards or something like that, and the producer really dismissed him, until someone told her Mark had been to Oxford and then she was all interested. Mark's not really very working class as far as I know but it's that assumption that you're thick, if you talk like that you've *gorra be.*

I don't think we used dialect at home, really. We never said 'Am you goin' down', we never talked like that, we didn't use the double negatives. We 'ad accents though, and words like 'bab.' I loved that, I loved the fact that I was called *bab*. I thought it was my name until I was about fourteen. 'Alright, Bab.' I loved that. My dad was from Birmingham, not the Black Country, and he'd say things like 'I'll go to Brierley 'ill and back' which were localish, I suppose. Or 'It'd dull over Bill's mother ennit.' But really we never said 'I ain't got none.' My mother would think that was rougher people than us.

With Birmingham, it's the tune and the attitude more than anything. Birmingham has its own personality just like all towns do. There is a certain negativity to it which people associate with slowness, whereas Liverpool, Cockney, Manchester are much faster. But I think the media is changing our perception about accents more than education in many ways. The old class divide is not as it was, because the things that we fought for in the Labour movement have been more or less achieved. I don't think there is a massive class divide. I think there's deprivation, but that's not the same thing. The change takes a long time though. I think it takes a long time to change, it will take ages and it's not going to suddenly change."

Meera Syal

Excerpt from *Anita and Me*

We walked back in silence, although papa insisted on holding my hand. If Anita's father, Roberto, had delivered a speech like that to her, she would have flicked her hair and said Bog Off! The words sat poised on the tip of my tongue all the way home. I did not have the courage to free them, but I imagined their effect and the image made me giddy.

I soon found out where my divided loyalties really lay, and it happened that afternoon when Pinky and Baby arrived. Auntie Shaila had decided to come early to help mama with the cooking for the evening meal, 'As she never gets any rest with that *munda* on her back all the day . . . Still, such a chumpy-sweetie pie he is...' What I had not bargained for was that she would drag along her two docile daughters who had once been my friends but whose presence now made me groan inwardly as they carefully got out of Auntie Shaila's Hillman Imp.

'Some company for you Meena beti!' Auntie Shaila trilled as she swept past me in a cloud of perfume and coriander. 'Why don't you show them round, huh? Go to the park, Baby loves swings, don't you, beti?'

Baby nodded shyly, hiding behind Pinky as usual, looking to her to answer for her. Once the adults had disappeared into the house, I stopped pretending I was vaguely pleased to see them and stared at them moodily. They were in matching outfits again, pink jumpers with hearts and daisies around the neck, jeans with a carefully ironed crease running down the legs, long black hair in bunches, held together with cutesy plastic bobbles. Pinky was my age, Baby a year younger, and they looked to me like infants.

'Hello Meena. Shall we go to the park then?' Even Pinky's voice set my teeth on edge, a soft pliant whine with a lilt of Punjabi in it, the over-pronunciation of the consonants, the way every sentence rose at the end so everything became a question, forcing you to answer and join in.

'No!' I spat back, furious that my afternoon plans of strolling up to Sherrie's farm with Anita had been ruined.

Looking at Pinky and Baby's timid, apprehensive faces, I knew Anita would enjoy snacking on their insecurities, their obvious lack of Wench potential. If anything, they were too easy a target, mere hors d'oeuvres for Anita's appetite. I also knew that if I had any sense of mercy I should bundle them both into the house and leave them in front of the television, their purity intact. But it was too late; Anita was standing at my front gate in a skirt that barely covered her thighs and one of her mum's old cardigans which had two saggy pouches at the front, like deflated balloons, where Deirdre's boobs should have been.

'Am yow comin' then, our Meena?' Anita's tone was deceptively gentle, she stood back slightly, sluttishly, and enjoyed the sight of Pinky and Baby shrinking back from her cocky gaze.

'Me cousins are here,' I said sullenly, ignoring the hurt realisation that was spreading over their faces. 'I'm supposed to look after em ...'

I left the unspoken question hanging in the warm afternoon air. An aeroplane passed silently above our heads, unzipping the blue sky with a thin vapour trail.

'Yow'll have to bring 'em then, won't ya?' Anita said lazily, already turning away, knowing we would all follow.

I pulled Pinky to one side and hissed in her ear, 'Yow can come with uz, right, but don't say nothin' and don't do nothin' and don't show me up, gorrit?'

Pinky swallowed and nodded, and then said, 'Meena didi, why are you speaking so strangely?' 'Coz this ain't naff old Wolverhampton anymore,' I said. 'This, Pinky, is Tollington. Right?'

Anita and I linked arms and sauntered down the hill, past the terraced houses and overflowing gardens where the occasional OAP would lift her head from her sunflowers and ornamental wells to nod at us as we passed. Their gazes lingered a little longer on Pinky and Baby whom I could hear pitter-pattering behind us at a respectable distance, and to my annoyance, I could feel the pensioners sigh and beam at my cousins in approval, uplifted by this vision of pretty little sisters in matching separates and coordinated dimples. We paused, as we always did, outside Mr Ormerod's shop window and shared a reverential moment of worship, faced with the tempting array of sweets which shamelessly flaunted themselves at us from the safety of their fat glass jars. I waited for Anita to go inside, as she always did, and wondered briefly where she got the money from for the sticky picnic we would always share in the long grass next to Sherrie's paddock.

'No, yow come in as well, Meena,' Anita said. I shot Pinky and Baby a Stay There glance but they ignored it, and followed us in warily, still holding hands. Mr Ormerod was shuffling around in the back room of the shop, when he spoke his voice sounded strained as if he were lifting something heavy. 'Be with you in a tick!' he shouted cheerily. Anita quickly leaned over the shop counter and grabbed handfuls of the loose confectionery that was always laid out in a small wooden tray, each assortment in its own snug box – cherry lips, sherbet flying saucers, chocolate spanners, edible necklaces made up of tiny pastel-coloured discs, white mice with licorice whiskers. All of them disappeared into the depths of Anita's cardigan pockets and for the first time, I realised why she wore these voluminous woollies.

'Goo on Meena!' she hissed, indicating I should help myself while the coast was clear. I glanced at Pinky and Baby who were staring at Anita as if she'd just deposited a turd on top of the shop counter. Pinky had a whole fist stuffed in her mouth, the other hand was clamped over Baby's eyes, and both of them looked close to tears. My hand hovered over a pile of marzipan bananas. I did not know why it trembled so much. And then suddenly Mr Ormerod appeared from the back room and I confidently picked up a banana from the top of the heap and laid it before him. He examined it quizzically. It looked ridiculous and lonely, a single unnaturally yellow smear on his sparkling glass counter. He looked up slowly at me, his eyes hardening.

'This all you want, chick?' 'Yes please, Mr Ormerod,' I said confidently. I did not dare to look at Anita who was standing, legs akimbo, hands in her pockets, checking her booty, a knowing grin plastered on her face.

Mr Ormerod swivelled round to face her and his polite smile became an obvious sneer. 'Don't suppose you will be buying anything, will you, Miss Anita Rutter?'

'Nah, got no money have I, Mr Ormerod,' she grinned back.

A muscle in Mr Ormerod's cheek began twitching slightly, he gripped the edge of the counter for a moment and the tips of his heavy-lobed ears went bright red. He was looking straight at Anita's bulging pockets and she knew he was; she was daring him to challenge her. Mr Ormerod was having a moral crisis, that was obvious. He had to somehow square Thou Shalt Not Steal with Suffer the Children to Come to Me, his desperation to be the most holy and charitable man in Tollington with the strong desire he now felt to smack Anita Rutter into the middle of next week. For a horrible moment, I feared he was going to keel over, but then he exhaled noisily and turned to me briskly with an open palm. 'Ha'penny please, Meena chick.'

Of course I had not brought any money with me, I never had to whenever I went out with Anita, and I suddenly felt cheap and childish that I had lived off her for all this time and had never appreciated all the risks she had taken to keep us both in pop, sweets and comics. I shifted my feet and let my gaze wander away from Mr Ormerod's still waiting palm until it rested on a small tin can next to the cash till on the counter. It was not a proper collection box, you could tell it was a former soup can masquerading as an official charitable receptacle, and besides, the slot in the top for coins was far too big. Someone had clumsily gouged the slot with a knife, so it was just as easy to take money out as put it in ... It was when I read the label that I decided to do it; a homemade label on lined paper in blue biro and Mr Ormerod's tense, tiny scrawl, 'BABIES IN AFRICA; PLEASE GIVE!'

'Mr Ormerod, I've just remembered,' I said clearly. 'Me mom wanted some Brasso ... yow know, that polish stuff. Have yow got any?'

I could feel Pinky and Baby at the back of me who had suddenly gone completely still, sniffing trouble in the air, and from the side, I felt Anita's knowing smile warm up my face like a spotlight.

'Ar, I have got some .... It's out back, just a mo chick ...' said Mr Ormerod, his voice back in its usual chirpy chappie mode, reassured that I was buying something else besides the marzipan banana. The minute the tailcoats of his brown overall disappeared into the stock room, I plucked the can from the counter and began emptying its contents into my skirt, which Anita, unbidden, held out like an apron.

'Get the shillins! Quick, Meena!' she whispered. I shook furiously but there was some kind of log jam round the slot. I could see a fair bit of silver inside, sixpences and florins in amongst the threepenny bits and pennies, but all that came out was two shillings and a couple of farthings. Then I heard a muffled clang from the stock room. Mr Ormerod was replacing the small foot stool he kept to get to the high shelves, so I pocketed the two shillings, grasped the tin and stuffed it down the back of Baby's soft pink jumper. She was about to squeak in alarm but swallowed it as I brought my face inches from hers. 'Yow say anythin, and yow'm dead, Baby.'

Mr Ormerod was back behind the counter, brandishing a small pot of Brasso. I handed him the two shillings and he smiled as he gave me back the change.

'Giz a couple more bananas then please,' I added nonchalantly.

As he counted the sweets into a small brown paper bag, he looked over my shoulder, from where I could hear Baby breathing heavily. 'You okay chick?' he asked suspiciously.

I turned to see large silent tears coursing down Baby's cheeks; she was standing as if someone had a gun to her back and one hand was clamped over her crotch. 'Oh, she needs the toilet, we'd better get home,' I said hurriedly and put a protective arm around Baby's shoulder, clasping the tin to her and did not let go until we were all halfway down the hill. Baby cried the whole way to Sherrie's farm, and was still snuffling when Anita and I settled down in the long grass to count our booty.

'Eighteen shillings and eight pence!' I breathed, enjoying the feel of the coins in my hand. 'We could buy all the top ten singles for that!'

'We could buy a ticket to London,' added Anita. 'We could just get up now and goo to London and no one would ever see us again.'

At this, Baby broke into fresh sobs and clung to Pinky's leg. 'Don't want to go to London, didi!' she wailed. 'Mummy will be angry! And I've got a maths test tomorrow!' 'Who said yow was coming anyway?' snapped Anita. I could see she was getting bored of having the moral majority following us around. Pinky finally spoke, she sounded so calm and grown up I wanted to gob on her T-bar sandals. 'The man in the shop. He will soon find out you have taken the tin. Then what will you do, Meena?'

'Then what will you do, Meena?' Anita mocked her, in a bad parody of Pinky's accent which came out as adenoidal Welsh. 'He won't know it was us. Unless you tell him,' I added, staring at Pinky.

'Us?' she blinked. 'But me and Baby...'

'Baby carried the tin didn't she?' I continued. 'That means you helped us doesn't it? That's what I'll tell the police anyway.' I finished off with a wink to Anita.

Pinky gulped and blinked rapidly for a few moments; I had not noticed before how long and luxuriant her eyelashes were, she looked like Bambi with a nervous tic. 'We will not tell, Meena,' she said finally. 'But we want to go home now.' And with that, she turned on her heel and led Baby through the long grass, both of them picking their way carefully through the cow pats and nettles like two old ladies negotiating a slalom.

'Hey, our Meena,' Anita said softly. 'Yow'm a real Wench. That was bostin what yow did. Yow can be joint leader with me now if yow want, you know, of our gang. Want to?' I nodded stupidly, too overcome to speak. I had earned my Wench Wings without even trying, and it had been so simple and natural, and what thrilled me most of all was that I did not feel at all guilty or ashamed. I had finally broken free, of what I did not quite know, but I felt my chest expand as if each rib had been a prison bar and they had all snapped slowly one by one, leaving my heart unfettered and drunk with space.

'Let's goo and buy summat, right now!' I said, heady with my triumph and Anita's praise.

Anita laughed wryly, 'Where? There's only one shop round here and we've just robbed it. We'd have to gerra bus into town and .. .' She glanced down the hill towards Pinky and Baby's retreating figures.

'Yeah, I know,' I sighed. 'I'd better go with em ... you know, in case they say summat,' and heaved myself to my feet whilst checking my bum for burrs.

'Yow gonna keep the tin then ... till we get to some proper shops?' Anita asked. 'Oh yeah, no problem,' I said, taking her arm in mine. No one would come looking for me. Only the ones who felt bad got caught, everybody knew that.

The knock at the door came just as we were about to serve supper. We kids, as usual, had been fed first and I was just wiping up a final mouthful of spinach with the favourite end of crispy chapatti that I always saved till last. The Aunties and mama were lining up a battalion of plates for papa and the Uncles who hovered around the entrance of the kitchen like hopeful domestic pets at a banquet. Pinky and Baby had not eaten anything, despite Auntie Shaila's loud protestations. 'You know how long it took me to puree this methi? Three hours, just because I know my betis like it smooth-smooth. And now you just sit there with a Pite-Moo...' (This was one of Auntie Shaila's favourite expressions, which meant the object of the insult had a face curdled up like the top of a yoghurt.) And indeed it was the perfect description of her daughters, who had both studiously avoided me since we had got back home.

I had hidden Mr Ormerod's tin amongst the rows of canned tomatoes in the bike shed, a perfect camouflage I had thought proudly, and had enjoyed a whole evening of being pinched and fussed over whilst opening my presents from the Uncles and Aunties. It had not been a bad haul either – the usual sick-making selection of frilly girlie dresses which all made me look like a biker wearing a collapsed meringue, but amongst these were a couple of books (*Look And Learn Compendium*, a *Jackie Annual*, a collection of Indian folk tales), and best of all, a bottle of perfume called Summer Daze, The Teenage Fragrance from Auntie Madhu. 'Now you are getting such a big lady, Meena, and maybe you won't come to my house smelling of cow's muck anymore,' she said kindly as I unwrapped it. Pinky and Baby had sat in a corner, regarding me with mournful moon-eyes and I knew they were hoping I would suddenly break down in filmy tears and confess my crime, to save all our souls. But their disapproval only made me more manic; the more they stared, the harder I giggled and quipped and chattered excitedly about nothing. I basked in their fear and bewilderment, it fed me and I welcomed it for it reaffirmed I was nothing like them, would never be them.

And then Mr Ormerod was standing at our front door and talking in whispers with papa, both of them throwing me sidelong glances, papa's face set like stone and Mr Ormerod's expression somewhere between wonder and disapproval as he scanned the glittering array of silks draped over the Aunties' magnificent bosoms.

'Please do come in Mr Ormerod,' said mama, wafting over to him holding out an empty plate, unaware of the gravity of the men's chat. 'We cannot allow a guest to leave hungry ... there is so much food, mountains!' she continued cheerily.

'Not now, Daljit,' said papa softly, staring hard at me. The chapatti in my mouth suddenly turned to a clump of barbed wire and I could not swallow. I hurried into the kitchen and spat out the end of my meal into the bin, running my tongue over my teeth which felt as if they were covered with a sour, greasy film.

Papa appeared at my elbow. 'Meena, I am going to ask you something and you had better not lie ...'

I affected an innocent expression, vaguely aware of Mr Ormerod, who had advanced a couple of feet into our front room and was gingerly holding a pakora between his fingers as if it was a small, sharp-toothed rodent.

'A collection tin has gone missing from Mr Ormerod's shop, a tin full of money for charity. Charity, Meena. Do you know anything about it?'

I opened my mouth to allow the story sitting on my lips to fly out and dazzle my papa, but stopped myself when I saw how furious he was. Both his eyebrows had joined together so he had one angry black line slashing his forehead like a scar and his usually light brown eyes were now black and impenetrable, glowing dark like embers. Then the enormity of what I had done hit me and a fear so powerful that I felt a few drops of wee land in my knicker gusset. I did the only possible thing and burst into tears.

'It was Baby!' I wailed. 'She wanted sweets and I didn't have money! I told her not to take it! She put it ... put it down her jumper! Honest! Ask her!'

I upped the volume of my wails and forced more snot out of my nose, waiting for papa to take me in his arms and tell me how sorry he was to have falsely accused me. Instead there was an endless pause and then, 'Are you lying? Because if you are ...'

'No papa! I swear! I got the tin! I hid it and I was going to take it back tomorrow! Honest!' At that moment, Mr Ormerod rushed into the kitchen and flung himself at the cold tap, turned it on and stuck his mouth under it, gulping like he'd just come back from a long desert trek. Mama bustled after him, wringing her hands fitfully. 'Oh please, Mr Ormerod! We do have glasses you know!' she fluttered, and then to papa, 'He bit on a green chilli ... poor man ...'

When Mr Ormerod stood up, there were beads of sweat

on his nose and he spoke in a breathy whisper, 'Please don't worry, Mrs Kumar ... I'll be right as rain. I mean, I eat English mustard but this has never happened to me before ...'

'I should have given you one of the children's snacks, they don't take to chillies either. Oh I feel so bad!' mama continued, until papa whispered something to her and she backed out gracefully, shutting the kitchen door behind her.

'Mr Ormerod,' papa said in a businesslike tone, 'I'm afraid one of our friend's daughters may have taken your tin and I don't want to embarrass her parents ... you understand.'

Mr Ormerod nodded, taking deep gulps of air, waving his hand in assent.

'But Meena said she managed to get the tin off her, so if I refund you the difference, maybe we can say no more about it, eh?'

Once Mr Ormerod had counted the contents, he told papa, 'It's just a couple of bob missing ... Let's leave it at that, shall we?'

But papa insisted on giving Mr Ormerod a ten-shilling note, pressing it into his hand in a fervent manner that left no room for disagreement. I mentally calculated how many sherbet saucers I could have got for ten shillings and felt aggrieved.

We must have been in the kitchen for a while because when we came out, the Uncles were finishing off their meal and the Aunties whispered curiously behind papa as he bade a still perspiring Mr Ormerod farewell. Mama raised questioning eyebrows at papa but he waved her away, indicating he could not talk whilst Auntie Shaila was at her side. That was a mistake because Auntie Shaila had radar built into her sari blouse and she collared papa soon afterwards in a comer, demanding to know what had gone on. Pinky and Baby were cuddled up together on the settee, testing each other on the capitals of Europe from one of the encyclopaedias I had been given at Christmas and had never read. They were completely unaware of Auntie Shaila's murderous glances and trembling gestures in their direction, but when it finally came to everyone to leave, Auntie Shaila merely threw their coats at them and shouted, 'Car! Now!' Pinky and Baby fumbled with their toggles and hoods nervously, now wide awake and alert.

Papa stopped Auntie Shaila at the door and pleaded with her in Punjabi, I caught the words for 'Gently ... children ... finished... ' none of which made any impression on Auntie Shaila.

I stood shivering in the doorway, watching Uncle Amman lead them to the car which was parked a little way up the lane. I told myself that if Pinky and Baby managed to get into the car without being told off, they were okay. The whole incident would be forgotten on the way home. I held my breath as Auntie Shaila held open the car door for them. Pinky got in first, Auntie Shaila did nothing. They were fine. Then as Baby got one leg into the car, Auntie Shaila cuffed her soundly on the back of her head, making her bangles jingle. Baby immediately burst into sobs, so Auntie Shalla hit her harder and then reached over her to slap any bit of Pinky that came within reach. 'So now you are becoming robbers? My own daughters?' Every word was punctuated with a swing, followed by a plaintive 'Mama nahin! Nahin mama!' 'So you think because you live here you can become like the goree girls? What next, huh? Boyfriends? Babies? You think you can spit in my face? Your own mother!' Auntie Shaila was still shouting over her shoulder as Uncle Amman pulled shakily away, forgetting to put his headlights on until he was halfway down the hill. I briefly saw Pinky and Baby silhouetted in the back of the car. They had their arms wrapped around each other and their heads lifted in silent wails, like they were howling at the stars.

I could not sleep that night and apparently neither could papa. I heard him tossing and turning next door, and then much later, through a hazy half-doze, heard his heavy footsteps going downstairs. The next morning he did not look at me and when Anita came calling at the hack gate, he picked up his newspaper and left the kitchen, slamming the door behind him.

Biographical Notes

Liz Berry was born in the Black Country and now lives in Birmingham. Her first book of poems, *Black Country* (Chatto 2014), described as a 'sooty, soaring hymn to her native West Midlands' (*The Guardian*) was a Poetry Book Society Recommendation, received a Somerset Maugham Award and won the Geoffrey Faber Memorial Award and Forward Prize for Best First Collection 2014. Her pamphlet *The Republic of Motherhood* (Chatto, 2018) was a Poetry Book Society Pamphlet choice and the title poem won the Forward Prize for Best Single Poem 2018.

Lisa Blower is the author of the short story collection *It's Gone Dark Over Bill's Mother's* (Myriad 2019) and a contributor to *Common People* edited by Kit de Waal. Her fiction has appeared in *The Guardian*, Comma Press anthologies, *The New Welsh Review, The Luminary, Short Story Sunday,* and on Radio 4. Her debut novel *Sitting Ducks* was shortlisted for the inaugural Arnold Bennett Prize 2017 and longlisted for *The Guardian* Not the Booker 2016.

Urszula Clark is Professor of English and Linguistics at Aston University, Birmingham. Born to Polish immigrant parents in Coventry, she has lived and worked in the West Midlands region for most of her life and taught English at both the Universities of Wolverhampton and Aston for over twenty-five years. Her research into accent and dialect in relation to the creative arts in the West Midlands has been funded by The Leverhulme Trust and The Economic and Social Science Research Council.

Jonathan Davidson is Chief Executive of Writing West Midlands, the West Midlands' regional literature development agency. His most recent publication is *On Poetry* (Smith|Doorstop, 2018).

R. M. Francis is a writer from the Black Country. He graduated from Teesside University with distinction in his Creative Writing MA and recently completed his PhD at the University of Wolverhampton. He's the author of five poetry Chapbook collections: *Transitions, Orpheus, Corvus' Burnt-wing Love Balm and Cure-All, Lamella* and *Fieldnotes from a Deep Topography of Dudley*. In 2020 Smokestack Books will publish his first full length collection and his debut novel is due with Wild Pressed Books. He is currently the inaugural David Bradshaw Writer in Residence at Oxford University.

Rupinder Kaur is a Birmingham born Panjabi poet with an immense love for South Asian arts. She sees writing and reading poetry as a way to liberate the soul. She published her debut collection, *Rooh,* with Verve Poetry Press in September 2018.

Steven Knight is a British screenwriter and film director. He read English Literature at University College, London, then worked as a copywriter/producer for a Birmingham advertising agency and started freelance writing for television. He is best known for screenplays he wrote for the films *Dirty Pretty Things* (2002) and *Eastern Promises* (2007), and directed as well as written the film *Locke* (2013). Knight has written for BBC's *Commercial Breakdown, The Detectives, Peaky Blinders* and *Taboo*. Other films based on screenplays that Knight has written include *The Hundred-Foot Journey* and *Pawn Sacrifice* both in 2014.

Paul McDonald is Course Leader for Creative Writing at the University of Wolverhampton. His novels include *Surviving Sting* (2001), *Kiss Me Softly Amy Turtle* (2004) and *Do I Love You?* (2008), with poetry collected in *The Right Suggestion* (1999), *Catch a Falling Tortoise* (2007) and *An Artist Goes Bananas* (2012). His scholarly work includes books on American literature, narratology, and flash fiction. Paul also has research interests in humour, taking pleasure in the fact that Googling 'the oldest joke in the world' throws up several hundred pages with his name on.

Roy McFarlane was born in Birmingham and is now living in the Black Country. He has held the role of Birmingham Poet Laureate (2010-2011) and Starbucks Poet in Residence (2009). In

2011 Roy McFarlane co-edited an anthology of poems *Celebrate Wha'? – Ten Black British Poets from the Midlands* and in 2012, he was featured in a major anthology of black and Asian poetry edited by Jackie Kay, James Procter, and Gemma Robinson: *Out of Bounds: British Black and Asian Poets*. His debut collection, *Beginning With Your Last Breath*, was published in 2016 and followed by a second collection, *The Healing Next Time*, both published by Nine Arches Press.

John Mills spent his working life teaching English in Stoke, a city he first graced with his presence in 1952. Since retiring he has focused more and more of his energies on poetry. As a prize winner who has been published in many online and print books and magazines he is never afraid to explore "The Dark Places" and can make you laugh or cry whilst bringing the essential out of the common place. Helen Mort describes his work as, "compassionate, bold and generous," and Jean Atkin described a recent reading of his as "Barnstorming".

Emma Purshouse left school in the early 1980s at the age of fifteen, initially working on various government schemes interspersed with bouts of extreme unemployment. She gave education another go as a mature student, attaining a BA from Wolverhampton University and an MA in creative writing from Manchester Met. For the last twelve years Emma has been making a living as a writer and performance poet. Her passion is writing about the working-class communities that she has lived in, often making use of Black Country dialect within her work. In 2017 she won the international Making Waves spoken-word poetry competition judged by Luke Wright. Emma co-runs a successful spoken-word night in the Black Country.

Roderick Smith is an actor/writer born and brought up in Northfield, Birmingham and now living in Suffolk. He learned his trade as an actor as an assistant stage manager at the Old Birmingham Rep. He has had an extensive theatre career appearing recently in the RSC productions of *Love's Labour's*

Lost, Christmas Truce and *Much Ado about Nothing* and at Birmingham Rep in *Tartuffe* and *I Knew You.* He has also been seen on TV many times in *Doctors, Holby City, The Rotters' Club, Judge John Deed, Dangerfield* etc. His writing credits include the short plays *Sunday Morning* and *K.Top* for the National Theatre Studio and *Fourteen Mouthfuls of Air* and *The Brummie Patrocleia* for the Arcola Theatre. He developed *Scenes from a Brummie Iliad* as a commission from the RSC literary department and has performed two parts of it as a one person piece at the INK Festival for new writing in 2018 and 2019.

Writer and actress **Meera Syal** was born in 1963 near Wolverhampton in the West Midlands and was educated at Manchester University where she read English and Drama. She co-wrote the script for *My Sister Wife,* a three-part BBC Television series, and wrote the film *Bhaji on the Beach* for Channel 4. She co-writes and is a cast member of the popular BBC Television comedy series *Goodness Gracious Me* and *The Kumars at No. 42.* She also works as a journalist and is a regular contributor to The Guardian. Her first novel, *Anita and Me* (1996), was shortlisted for the Guardian Fiction Prize and won a Betty Trask Award. Syal's second novel, *Life Isn't All Ha Ha Hee Hee* (1999), narrates the adventures of three young Asian women growing up in Britain. Meera Syal was awarded an MBE in 1997 and won the 'Media Personality of the Year' award at the Commission for Racial Equality's annual 'Race in the Media' awards (2000), as well as the EMMA (BT Ethnic and Multicultural Media Award) for Media Personality of the Year in 2001.

Julie Walters was born in Birmingham, England. She was an obedient daughter who trained to be a nurse at Queen Elizabeth Hospital to please her mother. Her desire to become an actress, however, overtook her and she left home to study drama at Manchester Poly. She landed major roles in the plays *Personal Services* and *Stepping Out*, both of which won her BAFTA nominations. Walters also received a Lawrence Olivier award nomination for her role in *Fool For Love*. Her movie career heated up with *Billy Elliot* (2000), for which she received a second Oscar nomination and won her second BAFTA Film award. She played Molly Weasley, Ron's mother, in all the *Harry Potter* films, and starred in *Calendar Girls* (2003). More recently, she reprised her role as Rosie in *Mamma Mia! Here We Go Again* (2018) and played the housekeeper, Ellen, in *Mary Poppins Returns* (2018).

Dr Benjamin Obadiah Iqbal Zephaniah was born and raised in Birmingham, England. His poetry is strongly influenced by the music and poetry of Jamaica and what he calls 'street politics'. He was not satisfied preaching about the sufferings of Black people to Black people, so he sought a wider mainstream audience. At the age of 22 he headed south to London where his first book *Pen Rhythm* was published by Page One Books. His mission was to take poetry everywhere, he hated the dead image that academia and the establishment had given poetry and proclaimed that he was out to popularise poetry by reaching people who did not read books, those that were keen on books could now witness a book coming to life on the stage. He has sixteen honorary doctorates and the Eailing Hospital in west London has named a wing after him in recognition of his work.

Acknowledgements

Liz Berry: poems from *Black Country* by Liz Berry, published by Chatto & Windus, reprinted by permission of The Random House Group Limited, © 2014.

Lisa Blower: by kind permission of the author, © Lisa Blower.

R. M. Francis: poems included by kind permission of the author, © R. M. Francis.

Rupinder Kaur: extract from *Rooh,* first published by Verve Poetry Press, © 2018.

Steven Knight: *Peaky Blinders* script included by kind permission of the author, © Steven Knight.

John Mills: poems included by kind permission of the author, © John Mills.

Paul McDonald: 'Yower Feyther is Jed' is an extract from *Kiss Me Softly Amy Turtle*, first published by Tindal Street, © 2014.
'Dow Fuck Wi Me, Yow Mutha!' is an extract from *Do I Love You?* first published by Tindal Street, © 2008. Permission granted by the author.

Roy McFarlane: 'Tipton' first published in *Beginning With Your Last Breath* by Nine Arches Press, © 2016.
'In a city of a hundred tongues' first published in *The Healing Next Time* by Nine Arches Press, © 2018.
Other poems included by kind permission of the author, © Roy McFarlane

Emma Purshouse: 'Flamingos in Dudley Zoo' and 'Two Sides of the Cut' were first published in *Close* by Offa's Press, © 2018.
'Vera considers life and the universe' was first published in *The Nailmaker's Daughter,* Offa's Press, © 2015.

Roderick Smith: extract from *Scenes from a Brummie Iliad* included by kind permission of the author, © Roderick Smith.

Meera Syal: extract from *Anita & Me* by Meera Syal, published by Flamingo, reprinted by permission of The Random House Group Limited, © 1996.

CHRISTMAS
THROUGH THE
KEYHOLE

The Bible Reading Fellowship
15 The Chambers, Vineyard
Abingdon OX14 3FE
brf.org.uk

The Bible Reading Fellowship (BRF) is a Registered Charity (233280)

ISBN 978 0 85746 520 7
First published 2017
10 9 8 7 6 5 4 3 2 1 0
All rights reserved

Acknowledgements
Unless otherwise stated, scripture quotations are taken from The New Revised
Standard Version of the Bible, Anglicised edition, copyright © 1989, 1995 by
the Division of Christian Education of the National Council of the Churches of Christ
in the United States of America. Used by permission. All rights reserved.

Scripture quotations taken from The Holy Bible, New International Version (Anglicised
edition) copyright © 1979, 1984, 2011 by Biblica. Used by permission of Hodder &
Stoughton Publishers, a Hachette UK company. All rights reserved. 'NIV' is a registered
trademark of Biblica. UK trademark number 1448790.

Extracts from the Authorised Version of the Bible (The King James Bible), the rights
in which are vested in the Crown, are reproduced by permission of the Crown's
Patentee, Cambridge University Press.

Every effort has been made to trace and contact copyright owners for material used
in this resource. We apologise for any inadvertent omissions or errors, and would
ask those concerned to contact us so that full acknowledgement can be made in
the future.

A catalogue record for this book is available from the British Library

Printed and bound by CPI Group (UK) Ltd, Croydon CR0 4YY

CHRISTMAS
THROUGH THE
KEYHOLE

Luke's glimpses of Advent

DEREK TIDBALL

Contents

Introduction

In our house, Christmas is always a time for music. We rejoice in going to concerts, buying new recordings of old carols with their familiar words and tunes, and equally welcome new compositions, or new collections of our favourite performers. Christmas without music is as inconceivable as Christmas without presents or turkey. Truth to tell, not all the old carols are good guides to the Christmas story. Some of them are shaped more by sentimentality and reflections of a later age than that of the first Christmas, while others contain some pleasant but misleading thoughts. Did baby Jesus really not cry, as 'Away in a Manger' claims? If he didn't, was he truly human? Were the Magi really three kings? And three ships sailing into land-locked Bethlehem is a little confusing. The original Christmas songs are better guides.

Soaked in the older scriptures of the Jewish people, the songs Luke records in his inspired Gospel – the songs of Mary, Zechariah, Simeon and the angels at Bethlehem – reveal the wondrous depths that for us 'in the town of David a Saviour has been born to you; he is the Messiah' (Luke 2:11, NIV). Their words are often those of the Old Testament; their style one of passionate yet reverent worship; their tone is one of humility; yet their rhythm indicates confident upbeat praise. To these songs we add, more briefly, the later reflective songs of John, Paul and Hebrews.

Let me ask a personal question. Do you like looking through keyholes? It is probably not the done thing to admit to such curiosity in polite company but the truth is that many of us are inquisitive. David Frost created a programme called *Through the Keyhole*, which took panellists around an anonymous celebrity's house, pointing out various features of the home and examining special possessions with a view to their guessing whose house it was. Often participants and viewers alike were left amazed at the riches they saw and at the uniqueness of some of the possessions. The programme migrated through various TV channels, and after 20 years still drew an audience of five million viewers when it came back under a new presenter at the time Frost died. It's just one small example of how we love to explore what lies behind someone's front door.

This book invites us to treat the songs of the Saviour's birth as keyholes through which we can spy amazing things. As we peep through our metaphorical keyholes, our eyes don't immediately settle on a crib or a crying infant. They lead us first to view the whole story of God's dealings with Israel that has led to the arrival of the Saviour.[1] They lead us through pain, agony and failure to discover the faithful mercy of God who, in sending a baby to Bethlehem, gives hope to his people and the wider world. We get to the manger, but only after negotiating our way through a longer story first.

The contestants on the TV show were encouraged to pick up some of the individual possessions, turn them over, consider them carefully and appreciate their value before moving on, eventually piecing their discoveries together into a collective picture of the person who owned the house. We will do the same with the lines of the various songs, not in order to fragment them but in order to give us a far greater appreciation of them and the one who caused them to be sung.

I am aware that it is common to use these songs of the Saviour's birth as the basis for meditations at Advent. Several books have been published in this area and, indeed, I myself have touched on them a little on a previous occasion. For that reason I have not referred to any of these other publications and not even looked back at my one previous book of Advent meditations. My concern has been to spy anew the story of the first Christmas through the keyhole of these songs and see afresh the rich and wonderful vision they give.

Each day's comment concludes with a text on which the reader is encouraged to meditate. To meditate is to fill our minds with truth from God or about God and to chew it over in our thinking. Five questions, among others, may help us to get started in meditation.

- What does this text mean?
- What does it teach me about God?
- How far do I believe what it states?
- What difficulties do I have with this text and how can I overcome them?
- How does it apply to me today?

Meditation requires us to use our minds but it is not an academic exercise. It is a spiritual exercise; all our thoughts are thought in the presence of God and should be turned into prayer and worship before him.[2]

Jesus – the hope of the needy

3–9 December

The Magnificat: Luke 1:46–55

And Mary said,

'My soul magnifies the Lord,
    and my spirit rejoices in God my Saviour,
for he has looked with favour on the lowliness of his servant.
    Surely, from now on all generations will call me blessed;
for the Mighty One has done great things for me,
    and holy is his name.
His mercy is for those who fear him
    from generation to generation.
He has shown strength with his arm;
    he has scattered the proud in the thoughts of their
    hearts.
He has brought down the powerful from their thrones,
    and lifted up the lowly;
he has filled the hungry with good things,
    and sent the rich away empty.
He has helped his servant Israel,
    in remembrance of his mercy,
according to the promise he made to our ancestors,
    to Abraham and to his descendants for ever.'

3 December

Daughter of grace

Do not be afraid, Mary, for you have found favour with God. And now you will conceive in your womb and bear a son and you will name him Jesus.
LUKE 1:30–31

Read Luke 1: 26–45.

The songs that rise to the top of the charts today are often not original creations, but fresh recordings by new artists of songs that have been around for a good time. A new voice and new arrangements, instruments and technology give songs from long ago a new lease of life. Sometimes triggered by the personal experience of the new artist, they are creative re-presentations to communicate to a changing situation. So it was, in part, with Mary's song.

Mary is one of a long line of women in Israel for whom giving birth is the crucial issue. From Sarah, through Rachel and Hannah, down to cousin Elizabeth, we learn of several childless women who miraculously conceive and whose children not only bring joy to the family but go on to play a critical role in securing the future of Israel. Unlike these women, Mary is not infertile. She's a young, vulnerable teenager who is a virgin (Luke 1:27, 34). Since she has not yet married, her virginity is a virtue, not a matter of shame. No wonder she is confused and 'troubled' (NIV) when the angel Gabriel brought news of her conceiving a child. With apparently no one to turn to, she goes to visit her older cousin Elizabeth, who is also surprisingly pregnant, knowing that they would at least have something in common. While she is there she bursts into song, the song we know as the Magnificat, because it glorifies the Lord.

Was Mary's song original? Not exactly. It shows great similarities to Hannah's song after she had given birth to Samuel (1 Samuel 2:1–10). Their songs celebrate God's gracious initiative in coming to the rescue of Israel through the birth of a child. Hannah's prayer 'represents a turning point in Israel's history. It closed an age which at times bordered on anarchy, a period of shame and humiliation… [and] opened the door to Israel's greatness.'[3] What happened under Samuel was merely a pointer to the greater achievements that would occur with the coming of Jesus.

Mary does not draw on Hannah's song alone. Line after line that cascades from her lips is drawn from the psalms, like Psalms 34, 35, 89 and 103. She may be young and female, and therefore probably uneducated, but she was obviously devout. These psalms would have been sung Sabbath after Sabbath in the synagogue in Nazareth and she had imbibed them deeply in her spirit. They had become a part of her. So, when the occasion arose, the appropriate words were all to hand and woven into a fresh new tapestry.

After the opening declaration ('My soul magnifies the Lord'), God is the subject of every sentence. The song does not boast that she is to become a mother, but rather that God, the Mighty One, is coming to the rescue, being merciful to Israel and proving faithful to his promise. We would have understood if the song expressed some angst about her sudden and unexpected condition. What would happen to her? What would people's reactions be? How would she cope? Yet the song is remarkably free from Mary's concerns and worries and is astonishingly focused on God. God must be the starting point for all our faith. If we have a wrong view of him, we will have a distorted and probably dysfunctional faith.

When she does briefly speak of herself, she is not the subject, not centre-stage. God remains the subject. He is the giver and she is the surprising recipient of his grace. Her 'lowliness' isn't pseudo-humility but actual fact. From what we know of her, as a young teenage girl, she wasn't significant in other people's eyes. When you also consider that she must have been relatively poor, judging by the offering she and Joseph made in the temple (Luke 2:24) and that she came from that backwater, Nazareth, you get the picture that she really was insignificant. She didn't merit any particular attention. Without qualification or entitlement, God chose her to be the mother of his incarnate son. She was 'blessed' indeed, as God poured his grace into her life.

What a remarkable thing for God to do, to trust the salvation of the world to a vulnerable, unwed teenage girl and, eventually, to Joseph, who was probably nothing much to be proud of either as a low-skilled, manual labourer from Nazareth. But that's the extraordinary thing about God. He has always worked that way. He didn't choose Israel for their strength or size (Deuteronomy 7:7–9) and he doesn't choose us because we're somebodies, but rather because we're nobodies (1 Corinthians 1:26–29). Mary fits the picture. She is honoured because she is the daughter of God's amazing grace.[4]

Like Mary, we have no cause to boast in ourselves but only in the grace of God. I wonder if, like her, we're so steeped in scripture that we have the vocabulary to express the wonder of that grace.

For reflection

Blessed are the poor in spirit, for theirs is the kingdom of heaven.
MATTHEW 5:3

4 December

Warrior God

For the Mighty One has done great things for me.
LUKE 1:49

The song of the daughter of grace wells up from the depth of her being. Her song is no mere performance. It has not been honed, practised and rehearsed over the months leading up to the grand opening night. While it is orchestrated and conducted by the unseen Spirit of God, it genuinely expresses the devotion of her heart and mind. She speaks of her 'soul' magnifying the Lord and her 'spirit' rejoicing in God. This is not an invitation to debate what part of her is her soul or her spirit. Like much Hebrew poetry, the lines run parallel, with the second reinforcing the first rather than trying to say anything new. It simply means she is praising God with the whole of her being. She's fulfilling, fortissimo, the command of Psalm 103:1, 'Bless the Lord, O my soul, and all that is within me, bless his holy name.'

Mary's opening words immediately make us aware of the ironic gulf she feels between her position and that of the one who has blessed her. She, the singer, is conscious of 'the lowliness' of her status as 'his servant', in contrast to the powerful status of the 'Mighty One' blessing her. Winston Churchill once apparently cruelly observed about Clement Atlee, his deputy during World War II (and after the war his successor as prime minister), 'Mr Atlee is a modest man. Indeed he has a lot to be modest about.' But this was Mary speaking not of someone else, but of herself. She had not expected anyone to take notice of her, still less the God of Abraham and of her ancestors. The people who God delights to bless are always those who, like

Mary, are not full of themselves and what they can offer to God, but those who come with empty hands for him to fill.

'The Mighty One' is simply 'the powerful' in the original Greek. He is dynamite (*dunatos* in Greek). As with all the descriptions of God Mary uses in the Magnificat, it is a term with a history. To speak of 'the Mighty One' was to speak of God as a warrior. It was a human way of speaking about the eternal God, but revealed him to be the one who intervened on behalf of his people Israel, the oppressed, the poor, the abused, the downtrodden and who stood up to bullies against injustice. God as a divine warrior is one of the central themes of the Old Testament. After their escape from Egypt, Israel rejoiced that, 'The Lord is a warrior' (Exodus 15:3). How else would they have been liberated from captivity? They certainly could not have done so relying on their own means. Down through the psalms and the prophets, Israel relied on God to fight for them, and on occasion found that God would, when they were living in disobedience, fight against them too. The theme wends its way down the years to Zephaniah's time.

> The Lord, your God, is in your midst,
> a warrior, who gives victory;
> he will rejoice over you with gladness,
> he will renew you in his love;
> he will exult over you with loud singing.
> ZEPHANIAH 3:17

In the comfortable Western world, we have something of an uneasy conscience about military conflicts and fighting wars. Who wouldn't rather use diplomacy and live in peace? But if we are among the many in our world for whom diplomacy doesn't work, whose buildings are bombed by an enemy out to destroy us, whose territory is occupied by an illegitimate power and who are subjected to slavery, pillage and rape, we'd see it differently. We'd long for a strong power to fight for us and deliver us. Such is the God of Israel, and of Mary.

When Zephaniah penned his words of promise, towards the end of Judah's existence as a separate kingdom, it seemed highly unlikely that they would become reality. It appeared much more probable that they were just pious words or wishful thinking on the prophet's part. But, now, a teenage girl from Nazareth declares that the words remain true and are about to be fulfilled, not only in her own life but for her people Israel. God was on the march again, to set them free from Satan and all who serve his will of oppression and destruction.

As often, the personal story and the wider story intertwine. The primary 'great thing' God had done for Mary was to bestow on her the honour of giving birth, though she was a virgin, to the Messiah who would deliver Israel. Can you speak of the 'great things' God has done for you?

For reflection

Who is the King of glory?
    The Lord, strong and mighty,
    The Lord, mighty in battle
PSALM 24:8

5 December

Holy God

Holy is his name.
LUKE 1:49

'What's in a name?' Juliet asked, protesting. 'That which we call a rose by any other name would smell as sweet.'[5] If names are arbitrary labels, Juliet was right. But in biblical times names were carefully chosen to express someone's character and to say something that encapsulated a person's identity. When Mary said of God 'holy is his name', she was not attaching a label to him but opening a window into his nature.

Black-and-white photos present their subjects by using a plain contrast in monochrome. Coloured photos, with their tints and shades, are often softer and subtler, but at the same time more complex in the eye of the beholder. The value of the black-and-white photo is that it confronts us with a clear, sharp picture. Holy is one of the Bible's black-and-white words, especially when used, as it frequently is, of God. The essence of holiness lies in difference. What is holy is sacred, set apart from the ordinary, clean and unsullied, and of special worth. When cooking pots and utensils were used in the tabernacle or temple they may have looked like the ones people used at home, but they were reserved for exclusive use in the worship of God, and deserved special care and attention, especially in regard to their quality and cleanliness.

To say that God is holy means that he is not like us and does not share our limitations and imperfections. He is awesome in his transcendent being. That's always the picture the holiness of God conveys. Yet a subject may be photographed from a number of different angles, so a number of its different aspects may be seen. So it is with our God's holiness.

When Mary proclaimed 'holy is his name', she was referring to God in his majesty. She was picking up the line before, where she had declared him 'the Mighty One', and nuancing it. She's drawing on the psalms, the hymnbook with which she'd have been familiar, like Psalm 99 which celebrates God as king, enthroned above the earth, 'exalted over all the peoples', great in the execution of his justice and righteous in all he does. The only logical response to such a God is to honour him in worship, to be awed by him and to sense our smallness, creatureliness and unworthiness. Rightly, therefore, the psalm invites people to 'Extol the Lord our God; worship at his footstool. Holy is he!' (Psalm 99:5).

In her own, different way, through the visitation of the angel, Mary was experiencing what Isaiah did when he visited the temple, in the year of King Uzziah's death, and encountered God presiding over his world and breaking into it in all his splendour and majesty. There he heard the song of the attendants at God's throne calling to each other:

> Holy, holy, holy is the Lord of hosts;
> the whole earth is full of his glory.
> ISAIAH 6:3

Perhaps because of this formative experience, Isaiah's favourite title for God is that he is 'the Holy one of Israel', which he uses over 25 times. To begin with, it bears a moral meaning. God is holy in stark contrast to his people's sinfulness and they will bear the brunt of his judgement. But in his later writing the emphasis shifts from judgement to salvation, and 'the Holy One of Israel' is seen as the redeemer who will deliver people from exile in Babylon. Isaiah borrows from Israel's history of the first exodus, from Egypt, to explain their future would lead to a second and greater exodus and to a new, purified remnant becoming a more glorious nation than before. This wouldn't come about by their own hands but through the intervention of their Saviour (Isaiah 43:3) and Redeemer (Isaiah 47:4; 48:17; 49:7) – the Holy One of Israel. Enemies and oppressors would come and abase themselves to Israel and their prosperity would make them the envy of the world (Isaiah 49:22–23; 55:5; 61:9).

As Israel's history unfolded, Isaiah's words only seem to have been partially fulfilled. Israel returned from exile under Cyrus, the Persian, but they struggled to rebuild a strong nation and never seemed to match the potential that Isaiah prophesied. But perhaps they were looking for the wrong sort of fulfilment. Mary believed that God was going to fulfil his promise and, somewhat astonishingly, that she would have a part in it. When her unique son, Jesus, began his ministry, people puzzled as to who he truly was. Those with access behind the scenes of the world, the demons, had no such quandary. They knew that he was 'the Holy One of God' (Mark 1:24; Luke 4:34). Eventually, the disciples agreed and came not only to believe but also to 'know' that Jesus was the Holy One of God himself in flesh and blood (John 6:69).

For reflection

For your Maker is your husband,
    the Lord of hosts is his name;
the Holy One of Israel is your Redeemer,
    the God of the whole earth he is called.

ISAIAH 54:5

6 December

Merciful God

**His mercy is for those who fear him
from generation to generation.**
LUKE 1:50

Mary's emphasis so far in her song has been the power of God. That could be somewhat daunting, not to say disturbing. If he really is such a big and powerful God, how can it be that he doesn't crush his fallen and rebellious creation as a steamroller crushes a nut? Mary has already given us a few clues. He uses his power as a saviour. He looks with favour on the lowly. But the real answer, without any inconsistency, is that he is not only a God of mighty holiness but also a God of abundant mercy. Just as any coin has two sides but forms one coin, so Mary's song introduces us to the two sides of God's united character. 'His mercy,' she sings, 'is for those who fear him.'

We're often in need of mercy – the response of compassion, understanding, pity, forbearance, kindness and, above all, free pardon – when we mess up. When we fail to be the loving, reliable spouse, or fail to fulfil our obligations at work or school, or let the sports team down by our indiscipline, or even break the speed limit, or… or… (fill in the blanks), we long for mercy. We want others to be brought to justice, but somehow we ourselves would prefer mercy to justice, knowing that, in Shakespeare's perceptive words, 'Though justice be thy plea consider this, that in the course of justice none of us should see salvation: we do pray for mercy.'[6] Thankfully, God's might is balanced with, constrained by and channelled through – or, better still, blended with – his mercy.

Mary did not invent the mercy of God. Anyone who says that in the Old Testament we're presented with a God who is angry, whereas in the New Testament we have a different God who is loving and merciful, has clearly not read the Old Testament or the New. Mercy is spoken of over 400 times in the Old Testament. From Exodus 34:6 onwards, God reveals himself to be 'the Lord, the Lord, a God merciful and gracious, slow to anger and abounding in steadfast love and faithfulness.' Mercy goes hand in hand with his steadfast love. Indeed, the Greek translation of the Old Testament (known as the Septuagint) translates 'steadfast love' as the Greek word for mercy. This steadfast, faithful, unfailing love takes us to the idea of the covenant.

The place where mercy is exercised is within the context of the covenant. We'll look into the covenant idea more next week. But a covenant is where we give ourselves to each other in a binding agreement, no matter what. God has entered into a covenant relationship with his people but it is not one between equal partners. He is God and we are his creatures. So God's promise to be our God entails our promise to obey his commands. And when we don't, it is possible, because he is merciful, for the broken relationship to be repaired. But it can never be repaired if we think our disobedience doesn't matter, or if our attitude is one of indifference or disrespect to him. That's why Mary says his mercy 'is for those who fear him'.

There is fear and fear, isn't there? Having lived for years by the sea I know there are those who fear it unhealthily and so never go near it. They cling tightly to the shore and consequently never know the enjoyment of swimming in it or sailing on it. That sort of cringing fear robs and represses a person. But a right fear of the sea is necessary if people are to find it a safe and life-giving environment rather than a life-robbing one. The sensible sailor does not put to sea without the proper equipment and appropriate clothing, or without having learned to navigate, to handle the boat and its instruments, and to consult the weather charts! Wise sailors fear the sea because they know its power and its potential dangers and show it proper respect. So it is with God. To fear him is not to cringe before him in abject servility. But it is to take him seriously, to respect his person, to submit to his authority, to obey his commands and to live to please him. If we live like that, then, when we have need and know ourselves to be undeserving, we find mercy freely available.

God's mercy is not scattered abroad willy-nilly. It is channelled to those who belong to the covenant and fear him.

Mary may well have been echoing the words of Psalm 103:17–18:

> But the steadfast love of the Lord is from everlasting to
>   everlasting
>   on those who fear him,
>   and his righteousness to children's children,
> to those who keep his covenant
>   and remember to do his commandments.

In the birth of Jesus, God was being true to himself and 'remembering to be merciful' (Luke 1:54, NIV).

For reflection

For judgement will be without mercy to anyone who has shown no mercy; mercy triumphs over judgement.
JAMES 2:13

7 December

Searching God

He has scattered the proud in the thoughts of their hearts.
LUKE 1:51

This morning I noticed that on almost every page of my daily newspaper there was a story about surveillance. Government documents leaked, CCTV cameras in our city centres, police forces using snooping devices, sensitive data being kept secret, a care worker caught robbing his client on video, and so it went on. In a culture of suspicion and mistrust, the desire to get at the truth feeds the burgeoning surveillance and enquiry industry. If only we knew what was really going on and what people really thought we could do something to right the wrongs and overcome our social problems, or so we think. And that's just at home. Broaden our horizons to take in wars and conflicts elsewhere and it soon becomes obvious that 'intelligence' is vital to any successful military operation.

We have already begun to see that in the Magnificat God, 'the Mighty One', is at war against rulers who oppress the hungry, poor and lowly. He has the advantage against his enemies because he searches 'the thoughts of their hearts'. Nothing is hidden from God. He does not only see their surface actions, or only hear their spin-filled and self-serving justification. He hears their heartbeat, knows their innermost thoughts and discerns their true motivations. They cannot hide from him. They may say their policies are in the best interests of the people they rule, but in reality the interests they serve are their own.

In biblical times, the heart, not the mind, was thought to be the seat of a person's will and the source of their motivation. Hence Proverbs 4:23 advises: 'Keep your heart with all vigilance, for from it flow the springs of life.' Yet the Bible is always realistic, and so knows that it is impossible for us to keep our hearts clean. As Jeremiah 17:9 despairingly comments, 'The heart is devious above all else; it is perverse – who can understand it?' Jeremiah pleaded with his people to 'wash your heart clean of wickedness' (4:14), but he knew the only adequate solution to people's corrupted hearts lay in God's intervention (31:33). Ezekiel agreed. Nothing less than the action of the divine surgeon performing a heart transplant on his people would be sufficient (Ezekiel 11:19).

Mary's concern is somewhat more limited. She rejoices that God has penetrated and exposed the wicked hearts of the rulers. They may try to cover up but they won't succeed and as a result God moves against them. When oppressors are defeated, as with Saddam Hussein in Iraq and Colonel Gaddafi in Libya, they will often go on the run. So here, the rulers who have been unmasked are displaced from their seats of power and 'scattered' with nothing more than their failed dreams to comfort them.

In singing this, Mary taps into another running theme about God's character. When Samuel sought King Saul's successor, he did what most of us would do and made up his mind which candidate was the most appropriate by using a set of external criteria. Were they striking in looks and charismatic in personality? Would people instinctively respect them as a leader? God had to remind Samuel not to look on their appearance or height since, 'the Lord does not see as mortals see; they look on the outward appearance, but the Lord looks on the heart' (1 Samuel 16:7).

While we keep this truth at arm's length, we feel safe with it. Indeed, we may derive some comfort from it, knowing that God will uncover the secret motivations of those who've done us wrong! But when we apply the truth to our own lives and hearts, it becomes more uncomfortable, even threatening. Do we have the same degree of confidence as David had when he wrote the following?

> O Lord, you have searched me and known me.
> You know when I sit down and when I rise up;
>   you discern my thoughts from far away.
> You search out my path and my lying down,
>   and are acquainted with all my ways.
> Even before a word is on my tongue,
>   O Lord, you know it completely...
> Such knowledge is too wonderful for me.
> PSALM 139:1–3, 6

And can we conclude, as he does, 'Search me, O God, and know my heart; test me and know my thoughts. See if there is any wicked way in me, and lead me in the way everlasting' (vv. 23–24)? Given what we know of David's personal life, this seems a bold step. Was he lacking in self-awareness? Was he arrogant? Didn't he understand how high the bar was set? Or was he, rather, rejoicing in God's watchful, providential eye over his life and trusting that the sacrifices he offered would make atonement for all the sins he committed. God's searching Spirit shines his light into the dark corners and innermost secrets of our lives, not to condemn us, but to stir us to turn from them and to seek fresh atonement from our Saviour.

For reflection

> I know, my God, that you search the heart, and take
> pleasure in uprightness... O Lord, the God of Abraham,
> Isaac, and Israel... direct [our] hearts towards you.
> 1 CHRONICLES 29:17–18

8 December

Revolutionary God

**He has brought down the powerful from their
thrones, and lifted up the lowly;
he has filled the hungry with good things
and sent the rich away empty.**
LUKE 1:52–53

My first visit to Romania was in Ceauşescu's day. The iron fist of
his communist rule seemed unassailable. Yet after just a couple of
years, the revolution happened and Ceauşescu was no more. A few
months later, I was back in Bucharest to join with Christians there
in the founding of the Evangelical Alliance of Romania and the
celebration of their liberty. Four thousand gathered in a government
assembly hall that had previously been a symbol of tyranny and
oppression. Most in the audience had experienced persecution, or
at least harassment, for their faith. They had been considered the
dross of society under Marxism, but now the nobodies had become
somebodies.

All that Mary's song has been celebrating about God comes together
in the astonishing claim that God is a revolutionary. He topples
the powerful from their thrones, condemns the rich to bankruptcy
and despatches the overfed from their sumptuous tables to the
wastelands. That truly is a political and economic revolution, and
we should never blunt its actual social implications. 'How can it be,'
I once heard a famous preacher ask, 'that these words are read in
gilded palaces every Christmas and the occupants do not quake with
fear?'

The problem is not simply that they have power, or are rich and well fed, but that they use their position to exploit others and demonstrate indifference to those in need. At root their sin is that of 'pride', which C.S. Lewis called 'the great sin' and the vice from which no one is free. 'It is,' he wrote, 'the complete anti-God state of mind' and 'the chief cause of misery in every nation and every family since the world began.' How so? Because, 'a proud man is always looking down on things and people: and, of course, as long as you are looking down, you cannot see something that is above you.'[7] Pride blanks God out. To be lowly and hungry, whatever else it entails is a disposition of the heart before God that is characterised by humility, unworthiness and a lack of entitlement.

We naturally think of 'lowly' and 'hungry' (and poor) as economic terms. But in Mary's day, and in Luke's Gospel, they have a wider reference to people who were 'defined above all by their dishonourable status, their exclusion'.[8] Mary's story personified that of Israel generally and the way they had been treated by the unjust, oppressive rulers of the world. Now God was going to intervene on their behalf and reverse their fortunes by bestowing his favour on them.

The claim that God is a revolutionary was anything but new. Delivering Israel from Egypt was an early act of revolution. God set the lowly slaves free, while the Egyptian authorities experienced the heavy hand of his judgement. He then fed the hungry escapees in the wilderness, en route to the land flowing with milk and honey.

Story after story shows God reversing fortunes by his gracious intervention. For Hannah, whose infertility placed her among the dishonoured, it was the birth of Samuel. Like Mary she prayed, 'The Lord… brings low, he also exalts. He raises up the poor from the dust; he lifts the needy from the ash heap, to make them… inherit a seat of honour' (1 Samuel 2:7–8). For Ruth it came through her marriage to Boaz. For Esther it came through the overthrow of Haman and promotion of Mordecai. For Job it came when God restored his fortunes, giving him 'twice as much as he had before' (Job 42:10). For David it came in the defeat of Goliath. For the exiles it came when they rose up from the dust and exchanged their mourning for joy, their rags for a 'mantle of praise' (Isaiah 61:3).

The birth of Jesus elevated the continuing story of God's revolution to a new plane. Luke repeatedly points out how, throughout his ministry, Jesus is defined by this gospel of reversal. He proclaims it as his mission in the synagogue in Nazareth (Luke 4:16–20), practises it in the attention he gives to the marginalised, demonstrates it when he mixes with tax collectors and sinners, displays it when he heals lepers and the disabled, and teaches it as he sits at the table in a Pharisee's house, and elsewhere too. Above all, the revolution is secured by his crucifixion when the powers (seen and unseen, human and demonic, who thought they ruled the world) rendered him utterly powerless, and tried to do away with him, only to discover that he had overthrown them by his embrace of death and powerful resurrection. The message of Jesus has gone on down the centuries toppling unjust regimes, lifting up the lowly and liberating the oppressed.

Once again, Mary's personal story embodies a wider story, and presents us with an amazing God who turns the world's normal status systems upside-down, showering grace on the insignificant. He is our only hope.

For reflection

God chose what is low and despised in the world, things that are not, to reduce to nothing things that are, so that no one might boast in the presence of God.
1 CORINTHIANS 1:28–29

9 December

Faithful God

He has helped his servant Israel,
  in remembrance of his mercy,
According to the promise he made to our ancestors,
  to Abraham and to his descendents for ever.
LUKE 1:54–55

In 1992, Hoover promised that those who bought a vacuum cleaner worth £100 or more would receive free airline tickets to America. Hoovers were snapped up and the company were overwhelmed. They were soon unable to fulfil their promises and some customers pursued them through the courts for years trying to get them to deliver on their offer. Some people make promises fraudulently, some manipulatively, and some with the best of intentions but then genuinely find they can't keep them. People can depend on promises and the results of broken promises can be catastrophic. Mary's song ends on a high note, celebrating God who is true to his promises.

The birth of Israel took place when God called Abram, as he was then called, to leave his home in the Chaldean city of Ur and journey to an unknown destination that God would eventually reveal to him. It took some faith for Abram to obey. The promise was that, in obeying, he would become the father of a great nation and blessed by God by becoming a famous and honoured name. The point of it all, though, was never to make Abram and his family prosperous for their own sakes, but rather that by blessing them, 'you will be a blessing' to 'all the families of the earth' (Genesis 12:2–3).

From the start the promise seems to have been thrown into doubt. By the time Abraham and Sarah had reached advanced old age, they didn't even have one legitimate son, let alone any evidence that they would be the progenitors of a great nation. Without even the most primitive of hospitals or IVF clinics, what hope was there that God would keep his promise? But God did.

Many times the promise seemed in jeopardy. Personal inadequacies and sibling rivalry threatened to destroy the family line almost before it got started. Facing starvation, they took the desperate step of going down into Egypt and to centuries of subjugation and slavery. Where then was God's promise to Abraham? Yet God had not forgotten them and after 430 years (Exodus 12:40–41) he set them free to kick-start the nation again. Through the wilderness years and the unstable period of the judges to the monarchy with its many disappointed hopes and the darkness of the Babylonian exile, the nation often hung by a thread and the promise of God seemed very precarious. Their sheer survival seemed a miracle, not least because they were never the most numerous nation on earth. True, there had been some bright moments, especially as they conquered Canaan and prospered under the rule of David and Solomon. But at best their history can be described as 'saw-toothed',[9] one day marching in triumph and the next plunged into disobedience and despair. Yet as Eugene Peterson, who uses the 'saw-toothed' imagery, remarks:

> But all the time, as we read that saw-toothed history, we realize something solid and steady: they are always God's people. God is steadfastly with them, in mercy and judgement, insistently gracious. We get the feeling that everything is done in the sure, certain environment of the God who redeems his people. As we learn that, we learn to live not by our feelings about God but by the facts of God.[10]

And the fact about God is that he never forgets his promise and, in his own good time, keeps his word. He is a reliable, trustworthy, faithful God.

Mary was a devout Jewish believer, but the thought that the birth of her child was going to be the supreme way in which God was going to keep his promise to Abraham was surely not the result of her own personal intuition, and still less her natural maternal ambition for her son. This was a revelation of the Holy Spirit. Jesus' family tree could be traced back to Abraham through Joseph (Matthew 1:1–17). But Joseph was an insignificant member of the lineage and nothing great could be expected from the son of a low-skilled carpenter from Nazareth. Yet God was keeping his promise never to forget his people and to make them a worldwide blessing.

And so it came to be. Through Jesus, Abraham's son, the nations of the world were blessed. They were blessed by having their relationship with God repaired; blessed by having their sins forgiven; blessed by the gift of the Holy Spirit, empowering them to change and live to please God; blessed in overcoming the racial, social, linguistic and gender barriers which divide people; and blessed by being reconciled to each other. They were blessed to be part of a global family that is composed today of 2.18 billion believers.[11]

In blessing one vulnerable teenage girl with a child, God was coming to the aid of a needy nation and an equally needy world and proving that he does keep his promises, even those made to Abraham centuries before.

For reflection

> They sing a new song:
> 'You are worthy...
> for you were slaughtered and by your blood you ransomed
>   for God
> saints from every tribe and language and people and nation.'
> REVELATION 5:9

Jesus – the redeemer of the world

10–17 December

The Benedictus: Luke 1:67–79

Then his father Zechariah was filled with the Holy Spirit and
spoke this prophecy:

'Blessed be the Lord God of Israel,
for he has looked favourably on his people and redeemed
them.
He has raised up a mighty saviour for us
in the house of his servant David,
as he spoke through the mouth of his holy prophets from of old,
that we would be saved from our enemies and from the
hand of all who hate us.
Thus he has shown the mercy promised to our ancestors,
and has remembered his holy covenant,
the oath that he swore to our ancestor Abraham,
to grant us that we, being rescued from the hands of our
enemies,
might serve him without fear, in holiness and righteousness
before him all our days.
And you, child, will be called the prophet of the Most High;
for you will go before the Lord to prepare his ways,
to give knowledge of salvation to his people
by the forgiveness of their sins.
By the tender mercy of our God,
the dawn from on high will break upon us,
to give light to those who sit in darkness and in the shadow
of death,
to guide our feet into the way of peace.'

10 December

Inspired song

Zechariah was filled with the Holy Spirit and spoke this prophecy.
LUKE 1:67

Even the hardest of hearts melt with wonder when a newborn baby comes into the world. But when the circumstances of the child's birth have been unusual and the path to their delivery precarious, there's even more cause for excitement. Parents go into celebration mode and often wonder whether the child will grow up to be special.

That was never truer than it was for a lovely old couple, Elizabeth and Zechariah, who lived in the hill country in Judea, and whose story is told intermittently in Luke 1. The one sorrow in their lives was that they had never had children in spite of praying for one (Luke 1:13). Sad as that was for them, their culture made it worse by assuming that childlessness was a sign of God's disapproval. Nothing could have been further from the truth in their case since they were devoted to God and obedient to his law (see Luke 1:6).

I'm not sure whether the fact that Zechariah was a priest made their devotion easier or harder – easier because they knew God's ways from the inside, or harder because of the weight of expectations on them. Either way, they didn't allow bitterness to cloud their lives. Perhaps centuries of spiritual breeding – they could both trace their ancestry back to Aaron – helped them to accept what God sent them without reservation.

There were some 18,000 priests in the temple, so they weren't all required to constantly be on duty. They mostly lived in the hill towns around Jerusalem and went up to serve during the major religious festivals and for the two other weeks of the year when they were rostered. Given the numbers, the one chosen to have the special privilege of offering incense in the holy place was decided by lot, so their choice was free from any human fixing or interference. It was a once-in-a-lifetime experience. So, the day Zechariah was chosen was always going to be a special day, but he had no idea just how special.

As Zechariah was performing his duty, he encountered an angel and, understandably, was overwhelmed with fear. Gabriel, the angel, delivered a message from God, which meant the people were kept waiting for Zechariah's reappearance. The message told him that he and Elizabeth's prayers were going to be answered and very late in life they were to have a child. So, they would stand in the succession of childless women in Israel's history like Sarah, Rebekah, Rachel, Samson's mother and Hannah. Each of their children had been special. Was Elizabeth and Zechariah's child to be special too?

Gabriel interpreted Zechariah's shock as disbelief and so throughout Elizabeth's pregnancy he was disciplined by being unable to speak. Only when the child was born and his name was in dispute and Zechariah firmly announced in writing that his name was John, did he recover his voice. Then 'he began to speak, praising God' (Luke 1:64). The song that came out of his mouth was no ordinary composition, although one wonders whether during the silent weeks of pregnancy he had thought deeply about the significance of their late arrival in the family. Whether under immediate and direct inspiration or whether through long, inner contemplation, this song was inspired by 'the Holy Spirit'.

We should note this experience of the Holy Spirit was not exclusive to Zechariah. Earlier, we read that Elizabeth 'was filled with the Holy Spirit' when she welcomed Mary to her home and prophesied that Mary's child was to be the Lord (Luke 1:39–45). In this couple, then, we have an anticipation of Pentecost when the Holy Spirit would be poured out equally on men and on women as a sign that the longed-for kingdom had arrived.

Zechariah's song runs parallel to Mary's song in two respects. First, they make similar claims about what God was doing as he stepped back into the history of Israel even if towards the end Zechariah brings John's role to the fore. Second, both Mary and Zechariah take their own experience and root it in the story of Israel. Their songs are keyholes through which to view the wider and longer story of God's relationship with his people.

Most parents think their child is going to be special, especially if they had never expected to have the child. In John's case, the parents know he is going to have a special part in Israel's story of salvation – the angel had made this clear. It was the neighbours who were left wondering, 'What then will this child become?' (Luke 1:66). They only had about 30 years to wait before they discovered the answer.

For reflection

In the last days it will be, God declares,
that I will pour out my Spirit upon all flesh,
    and your sons and your daughters shall prophesy…
Even upon my slaves, both men and women,
    in those days I will pour out my Spirit;
    and they shall prophesy

ACTS 2:17–18

11 December

Servant king

Blessed be the Lord God of Israel,
   for he has looked favourably on his people and redeemed
   them
He has raised up a mighty saviour for us
   in the house of his servant David.
LUKE 1:68–69

If Facebook had been around in Zechariah's day we would expect his entries to be full of pictures of his baby son, and perhaps his still-recovering wife as well. New parents are usually bursting with pride and want the world to be introduced to their new arrival. Zechariah's song was perhaps in some ways the ancient equivalent of Facebook. He was going to share his good news with anyone who would listen. But the beginning of Zechariah's song is something of a surprise. Rather than praising God for the birth of his son, he starts by praising God for the birth of a mighty saviour who would liberate God's people through an act of redemption. It clearly wasn't his son, John, who he had in mind. John comes later, because John plays only a small, if important, role in a greater story – that of the arrival of a Saviour. I'm not sure most of us would have had such a priority. Zechariah's godliness in putting the Saviour first is a challenge to our often self-absorbed communication and preoccupation with our own issues.

With broad brushstrokes and in quick succession the story of Israel comes tumbling out so that people can grasp the significance of what God was doing in their own day. Like Mary's song, Zechariah's was not a story about him and Elizabeth but about God and the new and gracious action he was taking on behalf of his people. Zechariah's inspired choice of words opens up the larger picture. God had 'looked favourably' on them or visited them, as he had done when they were enslaved in Egypt (Exodus 4:31). His 'visit' had led to their being 'redeemed', in other words set free from Egypt. Redemption was only ever secured through the payment of a price. In Egypt the price had been the offering of a Passover lamb or the death of the firstborn of the Egyptians (Exodus 12). In the current, developing story, redemption was at the cost of the Saviour's own life (Mark 10:45). The mention of redemption also flags up the practice of Jubilee, when the debts of people in Israel were wiped clean and debtors set free from their burdens and obligations (Leviticus 25).

The portrait that is emerging, then, is one of the God who liberates from oppressors. It's a busy picture, crowded with people who are part of the story. But one person stands out among the crowd and that is King David, unusually described here as a servant. The high point of Israel's history was the period of his rule. From his youth onwards he had challenged the Philistine enemies, like Goliath, who threatened the survival of the precarious and fledgling kingdom of Israel. When David became king he secured victory after victory against all sorts of enemies, leading them not only to enjoy freedom but also to forge a hitherto unknown unity and to experience an unprecedented prosperity. He was a 'horn of salvation', the horn being a common symbol of strength (2 Samuel 22:3; Psalm 18:2). Any subsequent rulers or deliverers were going to be measured against him. Furthermore, the legitimacy of any future ruler or deliverer was dependent on their coming from David's family. Except for that, their right to rule might be questionable.

The 'mighty saviour' whom Zechariah celebrates not only measures up to David but surpasses him in every way. Jesus is a son of King David, born in Bethlehem, the town of David (Luke 2:4, 11; John 7:42). As he worked his miracles the needy often addressed him as 'Lord, Son of David' (Matthew 15:22; 20:30–31; Luke 18:38–39). As people were trying to work him out, they queried, 'Can this be the Son of David?' (Matthew 12:23). He himself perplexed the religious establishment when he quoted Psalm 110:1 to them, which seemed to suggest that the Messiah would not only be a son of David but also recognised by David as his Lord (Luke 20:41–44). How could he be both, and how could Mary's son possibly fit the bill? Towards the end, the crowds in the temple acclaimed him as the Messiah, whom they thought of as a military liberator, crying, 'Hosanna to the Son of David! Blessed is the one who comes in the name of the Lord! Hosanna in the highest heaven!' (Matthew 21:9) and 'Blessed is the coming kingdom of our ancestor David!' (Mark 11:10).

All the hopes and dreams of Israel for David's kingdom to be revived and a new age of freedom and prosperity to be ushered in were about to be fulfilled. As the story of Jesus unfolded, it was discovered that David's reign would be surpassed and its nature transformed. His rule would not lead to a narrow, national victory against the Romans but would liberate men and women of every nation by him being a servant and surrendering to the cross.

For reflection

Remember Jesus Christ, raised from the dead, a descendant of David – that is my gospel.
2 TIMOTHY 2:8

12 December

Promising prophets

... as he spoke through the mouth of his holy prophets from of old
that we would be saved from our enemies and from the hand of all who hate us.
LUKE 1:70–71

It has become popular to say that the prophets were not foretellers but forth-tellers. They were more concerned, we are told, with denouncing the sin they saw around them and giving guidance to God's people about their present circumstances than they were with looking to the future. Like so many sayings, it is a half-truth, and Zechariah is concerned with the other half of the truth. They did prophesy the future, long before it happened.[12]

Take Isaiah. He often spoke in God's name about events that would happen in the distant future and his credibility, as well as God's, depended on his words coming true. God's ability to predict the future and then to bring it about set him apart from the idols Israel seemed attracted to, and made him unique, as Isaiah 48:3–5 among other scriptures claim. 'To whom will you liken me and make my equal, and compare me, as though we were alike?' God asked, before supplying his own answer: 'I am God, and there is no other; I am God, and there is no one like me, declaring the end from the beginning and from ancient times things not yet done' (Isaiah 46:5, 9–10).

Looking back, the apostles and Gospel writers saw several predictions of the coming Messiah that led them to believe Jesus was he.

- Isaiah 7:14 predicted a virgin, sometimes translated as young woman, who would 'bear a son, and shall name him Immanuel'. Matthew 1:22 claimed that was fulfilled in the birth of Jesus.
- Micah 5:2 predicted one who would rule Israel would be born in Bethlehem. Matthew 2:5–6 said that happened when Jesus was born.
- Jeremiah 23:5 predicted the king who would 'deal wisely, and… execute justice and righteousness in the land' would be from David's family. Matthew, Luke and Paul, in their different ways, were all concerned to point out this was so.
- Isaiah 9:2 foresaw the time when, 'The people who walked in darkness have seen a great light; those who lived in a land of deep darkness – on them light has shined.' And Isaiah 49:6 used the same imagery of light, with God's 'servant' becoming 'a light to the nations'. Luke 2:32 believed that was a pointer to Jesus.

There are further links to the prophets in the developing story.

- Matthew 2:15 connects his family's escape to Egypt and his return from there to Hosea 11:1.
- The massacre of the infants at Bethlehem (Matthew 2:16–19), which was sadly typical of Herod's paranoia, echoes Jeremiah 31:15.
- Mary, Joseph and Jesus settling back in Nazareth was seen as a fulfilment not of a single prophecy but of a prophetic theme.[13]

The predictions of the Old Testament prophets, then, deeply shaped the mindset of the early Christians and just as at one time it was said that all roads in England lead to London, so for them all roads about the future led to Jesus, who would deliver Israel from their enemies.

There is yet another prediction about a prophet to come that later became very significant in their attempt to understand who Jesus was. Moses assured his people that, 'The Lord your God will raise up for you a prophet like me from among your own people; you shall heed such a prophet' (Deuteronomy 18:15). Unlike many self-appointed and false prophets, this God-anointed prophet would command attention speaking only the very words of God. More than once, as the people in Jesus' day were trying to make sense of his identity, they edged towards the conclusion that Jesus was that prophet. For example, when Jesus fed the five thousand, John reports, 'When the people saw the sign that he had done, they began to say, "This is indeed the prophet who is to come into the world"' (John 6:14).[14]

Looking back, it seemed obvious that Jesus of Nazareth was the one the prophets had been speaking of. But looking forwards, would the prophets themselves have seen it that way? Perhaps not. They often spoke a deeper truth than they realised. Their prophecies sometimes seemed only to be partially fulfilled in their own lifetime or at the time they had envisaged. This partial fulfilment left people hungry for more. What they said was never untrue, but how it worked out was often surprising and pointed to a longer-term and greater future. As several have recently said, it was as if a father had offered his young son a horse and carriage for transport when he grew up, but eventually gave him a car because by the time the son had become an adult, cars had replaced such old-fashioned transport. Would any son object to the greater fulfilment of his father's promise? Would anyone criticise the father for not keeping his word? Surely not!

The prophets preached, predicted and promised. And Jesus delivered big-time on their claims.

For reflection

Then [Jesus] said to them, '... everything written about me in the law of Moses, the prophets, and the psalms must be fulfilled.' Then he opened their minds to understand the scriptures.
LUKE 24:44–45

13 December

Sacred covenant

Thus he has shown the mercy promised to our ancestors,
    and has remembered his holy covenant,
the oath that he swore to our ancestor Abraham.
LUKE 1:72–73

When we went to buy our house, which we'd been living in for some time as it came with my wife's job, the solicitor told us there were some covenants on it. That was news to us. What did that mean? What were they? And were they acceptable? We discovered that the covenant was a binding, unalterable agreement that had been stipulated when the house was built. One of them was a ban on keeping anything other than domestic pets on the property. Fortunately, we had no desire to keep llamas or lions, and teenage sons didn't count, so it wasn't an issue!

We don't talk much about covenants these days. We might come across them when buying property, as we did. We speak of marriage in terms of it being a covenant, but, given the frequency of divorce, the idea doesn't mean much to lots of people. We live in the age of contracts. And there is a world of difference between the two. Contracts are agreements between two parties about the provision of a defined service and they normally involve detailed rules about performance issues and specify how to get out of the contract legally when it no longer suits. Think football managers, and you get the picture. In contrast, covenants are relational and involve an open commitment between partners for them to give themselves to each other, no matter what, as the Marriage Service states. 'At the heart of the covenant, then, is a relationship between parties characterised by faithfulness and loyalty in love.'[15]

People spell them out in different ways, but all agree covenants were central to Israel's relationship with God, and, in fact, his relationship with the wider world. God made a covenant with Noah (Genesis 6—9), with Israel through Moses at Mount Sinai (Exodus 19—24), with David (2 Samuel 7) and promised a new form of covenant through the prophets Jeremiah and Ezekiel that didn't depend on the law but on the renewing of the heart (Jeremiah 31; Ezekiel 36). But the foundational covenant to which Israel reverted time and again was that made with Abraham. It was first set out in Genesis 12 and then confirmed and expanded in chapters 15 and 17. This covenant is the 'backbone'[16] of the longer story that connects all God's dealings with his people, and is the covenant that Zechariah highlights in his inspired song.

Through Abraham and his offspring, God was going to undo the devastation set in train by Adam and Eve's disobedience in Eden, which threatened to destroy creation, as Noah's days and Babel's tower tragically demonstrated. God chose Abraham's family to bring positive well-being ('blessing' is the biblical word, Genesis 12:2) to the world. That blessing was never intended to be exclusively reserved for one nation, let alone one family. The plan was that Abraham's family would channel it to the world. So God swore to make Abraham's family as numerous as the stars and settle them in a land they could call home (Genesis 15:1–7). Abraham was firmly convinced that God would keep his word, regardless of the practical impossibility of his doing so when as an elderly couple they were still childless. The covenant agreement was sealed through a curious ceremony which, while its rituals seem odd to us, made sense in the world of the time (Genesis 15:8–21). Later still, when even the birth of one child seemed doubtful, God reconfirmed the covenant. It was not a mistake, but 'an everlasting covenant' (Genesis 17:7). God would keep his promise. The covenant began with God's initiative. Abraham had no special credentials to qualify him for it. And yet, though it started as a result of God's unconditional grace, it required Abraham and his successors to walk in God's ways and keep his law.

Their repeated failure to invest in their side of the covenant relationship tried God's patience, but he refused to renege on his promise. He never forgot what he had said. His oath was sacred. So the covenant underwent various editions until the new covenant came into being through Jesus the Messiah. But it was the same principle running through history. The covenant inaugurated by Jesus is like having a new, all-singing, all-dancing TV in comparison with the snowy, small black-and-white set of the 1950s. The latest TV is altogether superior to the old one, but the principle of broadcasting pictures into people's homes is the same. Jesus' covenant is altogether superior to that of Abraham's but, as Paul explains in Romans 4, they're all connected by the need for faith in God's gracious salvation.

Zechariah knew that the covenant would have come to a humiliating end, except for the exodus from Egypt, which he brings to our attention in saying the oath God gave Abraham necessarily meant that 'we would be saved from our enemies and from the hand of all who hate us' (v. 71). And so it was to be in Jesus.

For reflection

> You will show faithfulness to Jacob
>   and unswerving loyalty to Abraham,
> as you have sworn to our ancestor
>   from the days of old.
> MICAH 7:20

14 December

Willing servants

... that we, being rescued from the hands of our enemies, might serve him without fear, in holiness and righteousness before him all our days.

LUKE 1:74–75

Before she married, one of my grandmothers used to work 'below stairs', as did many single young women of her day. She didn't work in a grand stately home, like Downton Abbey, but was nonetheless a domestic servant to a more modest middle-class family. Today the words 'serve', 'servant' and 'service' conjure up a range of ideas and often negative emotions. While we readily complain at poor service in a restaurant, we don't like the thought that people should be servants at all these days. Such a role belongs to a past age and demeans people.

Yet, when Zechariah celebrates God's salvation, which he traces down through the history of Israel, he unapologetically announces that the purpose of it all was so that Israel would 'serve him (God) without fear... all our days'. Salvation benefited Israel, but it was never simply for their comfort or ease, but so that God would have people to do his will and live for his glory in the world. Ironically, they were saved from oppressive slavery in order to become slaves of their liberating God.

Our qualms at the thought of being servants are perhaps unwarranted. First, because it depends who we serve. I've met a number of people who've been lowly servants as far as the contemporary social pecking order is concerned, but they're proud of their role because of whose servants they are. You can even see them stand tall and puff out their chests when talking about it. What greater position can there be for Israel, or for us, than to serve the Lord God, king of the universe? It's far better to be his lowly servant than to be the right-hand advisor of some useless idol!

Second, there's the nature of the service itself. Zechariah picks his words carefully. Avoiding the common word for service (*diakonein*) he chooses a word associated with priestly service (*lateurein*). In this way, Zechariah tells us that the service we render to God is akin to the priests serving in the temple. To serve is to worship. Saying this, we should bear in mind that the priests were punctilious about their service in the temple. Good intentions were not enough. Careful obedience was required if their service was to prove acceptable to God, as the disturbing stories about Nadab and Abihu (Leviticus 10:1–7) and about Uzzah illustrate (2 Samuel 6:1–11).

Here's another moment when we're looking through the keyhole and seeing a much bigger picture than we might have expected. Moses said to Pharaoh, 'Let my people go, so that they may worship me...' (Exodus 7:16). God's powerful act of liberation had always been for the purpose of having a people who would serve him.

Furthermore, God had never intended Israel to have a priesthood so much as to be a priesthood. Their calling was to be 'a priestly kingdom', as God clearly stated to Moses on Sinai (Exodus 19:6). Israel was to place itself wholly at the Lord's disposal, as the burnt offering symbolised when it was consumed by fire (Leviticus 1). Daily living was to be an act of worship lived in accordance with the covenant stipulations, uncontaminated by those who worshipped other gods, and of loving their neighbours as themselves. As priests, they were to be intercessors for the world around them, pleading to God on behalf of their neighbours and witnessing to their neighbours on behalf of God. This unique calling was the reason God had rescued them from Egypt and is a calling that had never been rescinded. Indeed, with the coming of Christ it was to be given a new significance in the light of his greater salvation affected through his death.

There are two ways to serve. One is to serve in a joyless, dutiful way, tinged with fear, like the older brother in the story we somewhat unwisely call 'the prodigal son'. The other is to serve in love, 'without fear', like the younger brother on his return home. The rabbis taught that it was far superior to serve God out of love than in fear.[17] Once we understand the depth of God's grace, love should banish fear from our service to our Saviour.[18]

Digging deeper, Zechariah says we serve 'in holiness and righteousness', pointing to the integrity of our service. Purity of heart needs to be matched by right action. The one without the other is deficient.[19] This section concludes with Zechariah emphasising that serving is an unending privilege. There's no sell-by date after which service is no longer advised, and no retirement date set after which service is no long required. The privilege of service lasts as long as we last, though its form may vary. It's not confined to our 20s, 40s or 60s but to the end of our days.

Preachers frequently used to say we are 'saved to serve'. The catchphrase may have become devalued through overuse but it expresses a profound biblical truth, perhaps more profound than many realised. Serving is indeed why we are saved.

For reflection

Choose this day whom you will serve... as for me and my household, we will serve the Lord.
JOSHUA 24:15

15 December

Pioneering prophet

**And you, child, will be called the prophet of the Most High;
for you will go before the Lord to prepare his ways.**
LUKE 1:76

At last we get to the son. Zechariah's song, supposedly celebrating the birth of his unexpected son, John, has taken a long time to reach what we might have expected to be its purpose. When he does get there, the focus is not on the miraculous circumstances of his birth but the momentous future that lies before him. Most parents expect their children to grow up to become Olympic athletes, Nobel prize winners, Premier League footballers or winners of *The X Factor*, depending on their tastes. But the claims Zechariah makes are second to none, except those made of Jesus himself.

Cousin John is to be 'called the prophet of the Most High'. Earlier in the song, Zechariah had spoken of a multitude of prophets (v. 70). But John was to be *the* prophet, not one among many, but in a class of his own. How so?

The Jewish expectation was that one day the Lord himself would return in person to the temple, finally bringing the heartache of their feeling of alienation from God to an end. People assumed that when God came in this way he would be on their side, vanquish their enemies and bring them to a new golden age of freedom, peace and prosperity. Despite all warnings, like those given by the prophets Amos (5:18–20) and Malachi (3:2), that this 'day of the Lord' may not prove as comforting to Israel as they glibly expected, the desire for

God's return not only persisted but intensified. Roman occupation only served to stoke the fires of hope.

While details of this day may have been sketchy, the prophets agreed on one particular point. A forerunner would prepare the Lord's visit. When they identified him, they knew the Lord himself was not far behind. God had announced through Malachi, 'See, I am sending my messenger to prepare the way before me, and the Lord whom you seek will suddenly come to his temple' (3:1). Similarly, Isaiah (40:3–5), quoted in Luke 3:4–6, had spoken of:

> The voice of one crying out in the wilderness:
> 'Prepare the way of the Lord,
>   make his paths straight.
> Every valley shall be filled,
>   and every mountain and hill shall be laid low,
> and the crooked shall be made straight,
>   and the rough ways made smooth;
> and all flesh shall see the salvation of God.'

Just as a town fills in the potholes, relays the tarmac, and repaints the street lamps when a member of the royal family comes to visit, so the prophets foresaw the entry of the Messiah to the world would be preceded by preparation that would smooth his coming and heighten people's awareness of his arrival.

Malachi had added one further detail about the forerunner. He named him as Elijah: 'Lo, I will send you the prophet Elijah before the great and terrible day of the Lord comes' (4:5). When John appeared with his bizarre lifestyle, radical preaching, demand for repentance and practice of baptism in the River Jordan, he reminded people of Elijah (compare 2 Kings 1:8). Zechariah, of course, knew all along that his son would play this role. He didn't need persuading. John's preaching signalled that the new kingdom was about to begin. 'The signs,' as Morna Hooker says, 'are all present; what comes next must be the long-awaited salvation.'[20]

Hence, John is the last of the prophets (with the exception of Jesus himself), the bridge to the new kingdom. After 400 years of prophetic silence, John cries out in the wilderness, not to revive the old ways of God's working – the continuous cycle of preaching, repentance, failure and salvation – but to be the voice that announced the arrival of the new era. It would be a day when God would re-establish his rule as king, pour out mercy and grace through his Son, and offer a genuine transformation of heart by his Spirit.

It was truly astonishing that John was content to play the part God had assigned to him and was concerned not to upstage. He had no desire to claim equality with his cousin Jesus, saying rather that he was unworthy to untie Jesus' sandals (Luke 3:16). He knew his part was limited but vital. He saw himself as the best man, whose only joy was in serving the bridegroom and who would do nothing to distract attention from the groom. Therefore, he said, it was necessary for Jesus to come centre stage and for him to fade away (John 3:26–30).

His role as the last of the prophets cost him his life. I wonder what Zechariah and Elizabeth, if they were still alive, thought of that. Had God been cruel to give them a son only to rob them of him too early? As a couple steeped in the stories of Israel, they knew that was often the fate of prophets. John was no exception. He'd done his job of preparing the way for the Messiah, and although there were struggles and questions en route, deep down all three would have rejoiced that he was chosen to 'go before the Lord'.

For reflection

He must increase, but I must decrease.
JOHN 3:30

16 December

Radical salvation

*... to give knowledge of salvation to his people
by the forgiveness of their sins.*
LUKE 1:77

Flying early one morning into Uganda's Entebbe airport stirred up all sorts of emotions. In July 1976 the most daring of rescue missions had been mounted there to free hostages, many of them Jewish, after their plane had been hijacked on a flight from Tel Aviv to Paris. The courageous surprise attack of their liberators lasted less than an hour and, against all odds, was successful, although the leader of the assault team and three of the 106 hostages were killed. But the rest were set free. Years later, when I was landing there, the evidence of the attack was still visible. It was an act of heroic salvation.

As I write, two cities are in the world's headlines – Aleppo and Mosul. By the time you read this other cities may be in the headlines, sadly for similar reasons. Both cities are under attack, both in need of liberation. In both cities the population want freedom. They long for the day when they will no longer be living in fear, under tyrannical regimes, without adequate food and water, and unable to go about their normal lives. They long to be free from suffering in all its forms: whether that which arises from insanitary conditions and disease, from the cruel and unpredictable torture meted out unjustly by their rulers, or from the sudden onset of bomb strikes, which leaves some dead, more injured and many homeless, as their buildings are destroyed. For them, salvation means being rescued and set free from such a horrific and tragic situation.

Zechariah tells us how John is going to prepare the way for the Messiah. He is going to do it by alerting his audience to the fact that God's rescue mission is underway and his salvation will soon be experienced. But what did he mean by salvation? It's here the song takes yet another surprising turn.

John's listeners would have thought along the same lines as the captives in Entebbe, Mosul or Aleppo. Salvation was God's promise that he would drive out their enemies and set them free to enjoy peaceful and whole lives. The story of Israel, to which Zechariah had already alluded, led them down that path. But here's the surprise. The salvation that John will preach, and his cousin Jesus will deliver, is not deliverance from a militaristic oppressor – Rome – as they thought, or about political liberation, or about restoring nationalistic pride. This salvation, Zechariah says, is about 'the forgiveness of sins'. Zechariah was right. When John began to preach, what did he say? According to Luke's sources, he 'went into all the region around the Jordan, proclaiming a baptism of repentance *for the forgiveness of sins*' (Luke 3:3, emphasis added).

Many might have seen that as a bit of a let down. They were expecting literally to see their enemies driven out and for an entirely new political day to dawn. But John the Baptist seems to have altered the goalposts in pointing to people's own need for forgiveness and a new beginning with God. How does it all fit? By spiritualising it, has he engaged in a sleight of hand that means it is all less real and less tangible and more inward and otherworldly?

In Colossians, Paul helps us understand what this means as he presents the gospel in terms of whose government we are under (Colossians 1:13–14). Political realities are a picture of greater spiritual realities. The Colossians, Paul explains, used to live under an illegitimate and oppressive regime, which he calls the kingdom or 'power of darkness', but God had freed them from its tyranny and they've been 'transferred... into the kingdom of his beloved Son'. His act of salvation, or redemption, addressed the underlying cause of their lack of freedom. In sinning, we place ourselves under an alien, destructive power, the power of darkness. Salvation comes when sin is forgiven and the alienating power that holds us captive no longer has any grounds for doing so. As in any act of redemption or any daring act of freedom, like Entebbe, there is a price to pay. In our case, Jesus paid it in full on the cross (Colossians 2:14–15).

Forgiveness of sin, then, is not an incidental outcome but the essential core of salvation. Our real need is freedom from sin and Satan and this is the key to other freedoms. Repeatedly, Luke connects salvation with the forgiveness of sin in his Gospel, even when talking to the poor and the victims.[21] Only forgiveness truly liberates us from our captors. Zechariah, John and Jesus didn't get the message of salvation wrong. They understood it more deeply than many of us do. Hence, the church is still about ensuring that 'repentance and forgiveness of sins is to be proclaimed... to all nations...' (Luke 24:47).

For reflection

[Jesus said to Paul,] 'I will rescue you from your people and from the Gentiles – to whom I am sending you to open their eyes so that they may turn from darkness to light and from the power of Satan to God, so that they may receive forgiveness of sins and a place among those who are sanctified by faith in me.'

ACTS 26:17–18

17 December

Spreading light

By the tender mercy of our God,
the dawn from on high will break upon us,
to give light to those who sit in darkness and in the shadow
of death,
to guide our feet into the way of peace.
LUKE 1:78–79

The first recorded words of God are, 'Let there be light' (Genesis 1:3). Nearly the last recorded words of the Bible celebrate the redundancy of all other sources of light from the new creation, since 'the Lord God will be their light' (Revelation 22:5). 'Between these two beacons the imagery of light makes nearly two hundred appearances and light emerges as a major and varied symbol.'[22] It is not surprising, then, that light plays a key role in the Christmas story.

From our own experience, we can readily understand why darkness is seen as negative. I cannot conceive what it is like to live in the Arctic Circle, where it never gets light for six months of the year. Darkness hides dangers under its cloak. It prevents us from finding the way. It leads to confusion. It isolates people from each other. People commit crimes 'under cover of darkness'. Sick and elderly people often struggle with sleepless nights and long for the morning. Not for nothing is darkness associated with suffering, evil and death.

Looking back on their story, Israel could be described as a 'people who walked in darkness' (Isaiah 9:2). To Job, their leaders were devoid of sense and were groping 'in the dark without light' and staggering 'like a drunkard' (Job 12:24–25). Individuals personally 'sat in darkness and in gloom, prisoners in misery...' because they refused to obey God's words (Psalm 107:10–11), while the nation as a whole could sometimes be described as prisoners in a darkened underground dungeon. They knew what it was to walk through 'the darkest valley' and to fear evil (Psalm 23:4).

The prophets had looked forward to the ending of darkness and the breaking of a new day for centuries. When Isaiah honestly admitted Israel sat in darkness, it was not to condemn them to do so forever. His point was not to add to their guilt but to provide them with hope. They were the very people who 'have seen a great light... on them the light has shined' (Isaiah 9:2). In some of his writing, he is so convinced of the light dawning that he speaks as if it has already happened.

> Arise, shine; for your light has come,
>   and the glory of the Lord has risen upon you.
> For darkness shall cover the earth,
>   and thick darkness the peoples;
> but the Lord will arise upon you,
>   and his glory will appear over you.
> Nations shall come to your light,
>   and kings to the brightness of your dawn
> ISAIAH 60:1–3

Elsewhere Isaiah speaks of it as a future event, tied up with the coming of a servant who would be 'a light to the nations' and who would 'bring out the prisoners from the dungeon, from the prison those who sit in darkness' (42:7). Malachi shared that future hope and looked forward to the day when those who revered God's name would witness the rising of 'the sun of righteousness... with healing in its wings' (4:2).

With John's birth that new day was dawning. The shadows would be banished and the darkness defeated. He would herald the coming of Jesus 'the light of the world' (John 8:12), the unique Son of God who himself was 'light and in him there is no darkness' (1 John 1:5). Throughout his ministry, he overcame the darkness that had stalked people, whether the darkness of sin, brokenness, lying, fear, religious prejudice, hypocrisy, the literal darkness of blindness, or death. The darkness was determined not to yield to the light and time and again sought to defeat it. Its ultimate onslaught against the light was mounted when it took the loveliest, most genuine and compassionate life there had ever been and tried to snuff it out on a Roman cross. The sun itself ceased to shine that day. But the darkness could not win. 'At early dawn', when the light began to spread on the first day of the week after the crucifixion, as the women arrived at the tomb of Jesus they discovered the darkness had finally been defeated.

People did not deserve the coming of this light. If God had been unbending in his justice, he would have left people meandering in confusion in the darkness they had brought on themselves. But the light came because he is a God of 'tender mercy' who desired to bring people out of the fog of their alienation from him and guide them into the wholesome paths of peace. To have God's peace is to know God's favour on our lives and his rich blessing in all its fullness. To be guided into these paths requires light, a light we cannot supply ourselves, but the light of truth and the gospel, which our gracious God has provided for us.

Looking through the keyhole, Zechariah knew that with the birth of his son, John, the day was dawning and the light was entering the world.

For reflection

Do all things without murmuring and arguing, so that you may be blameless and innocent, children of God without blemish in the midst of a crooked and perverse generation, in which you shine like stars in the world.

PHILIPPIANS 2:14–15

Jesus – the joy of the earth

18–23 December

The Gloria: Luke 2:13–14

And suddenly there was with the angel a multitude of the heavenly host, praising God and saying,

'Glory to God in the highest heaven
  and on earth peace among those whom he favours!'

18 December

Angels

And suddenly there was with the angel a multitude of the heavenly host, praising God...
LUKE 2:13

Uninvited angels keep cropping up in the Christmas story like gatecrashers from another world. Gabriel alarms Zechariah as he goes about his priestly duty with the news that he's going to have a son. He visits Mary in Nazareth with the even more remarkable news that she is pregnant with the Messiah. Then the skies above the hills of Bethlehem are torn open as an angel announces the good news of a Saviour born in the town nearby. Was this also Gabriel? Luke doesn't tell us the angel's name so it might have been a celestial colleague. It was only later that Gabriel seems to have been promoted to the rank of archangel. When he's first introduced in the Bible he is only described as a man (Daniel 9:21).

It's curious that in a world of increasing and unyielding secularism, belief in angels has grown rather than died. According to one recent survey, '31 per cent of people in Britain believe in angels and 29 per cent believe that a guardian angel watches over them.'[23] The spirituality shelves in our bookshops groan under the weight of books about angels under such titles as *The Year with Angels*, *How to Hear your Angels* and *A Message of Hope from Angels*. Angels have gone commercial!

Mention angels and you'll soon be told stories about people's experiences of them, some quite believable and some frankly weird.

Those that have the ring of truth about them are those that talk of strangers making a surprising appearance to assist or guide someone when no human help was available. My wife recently reminded me of just such an episode in our own lives. So, they're not to be dismissed lightly. But who are they?

Angels appeared early on to Abraham (Genesis 18:1–2), and keep appearing in the Bible's story. They visit Jacob (Genesis 32:1), Gideon (Judges 6:11–12), Samson's parents (Judges 13:1–23), Elijah (1 Kings 19:4–9), Daniel (Daniel 9:20–27) and a host of others. They are servants of God who deliver a message to people that often results in a change of direction in life. Given that, it would be extraordinary if they did not appear in the Christmas story (or, for that matter, in the story of the resurrection). They don't dress in a particular way and often seem quite ordinarily human, although occasionally they are described as dressed in white or have an aura of light about them. It is a far cry from the great works of Medieval or Renaissance art, which picture them as 'chubby toddlers'[24] or enveloped in wings.

Angels have two major roles. First, as messengers of God they deliver news and, second, they lead those around God's throne in offering him honour and praise. Both of these flow together in their appearances to do with the birth of Jesus. The solitary angel, mentioned in Luke 2:10, announces to the startled shepherds, 'Do not be afraid' (as if encountering celestial visitors was an everyday occurrence!). 'For see – I am bringing you good news of great joy for all the people: to you is born this day in the city of David a Saviour, who is the Messiah, the Lord.' But he is soon joined by a choir of angels, 'a multitude of the heavenly host', who respond to the announcement with songs of praise.

Speaking in human terms, God is pictured as having a heavenly council, just as a royal sovereign might have. Some are advisers (Psalm 82:1; Job 1:6); others undertake different responsibilities. The winged cherubim attend the throne of God and transport it (Psalm 80:1; Ezekiel 10:1–22). The seraphim, who are also winged creatures, are mentioned just once, in Isaiah 6, as offering God praise. The angels form the 'heavenly host' and we catch glimpses of them worshipping around the throne, the fullest of which is seen in Revelation 4 and 5. It's easy to develop an unhealthy fascination with these creatures. Some want to tie down more precisely what they look like or to have a greater definition of their responsibilities. Some want to organise them into hierarchies and sort out what ranks can be given to them. But the Bible shows no such inclination. That they come from God and attend God's throne is enough.

So what's the point of it all? One of the things this teaches us is that the distance between earth and heaven is not so great, and the boundaries between them not so fixed, as we often think. The angels didn't have to travel for months from the other side of the universe to visit planet earth. Heaven is nearby and the curtain between heaven and earth is thin. Heaven is where God rules over and intervenes in the affairs of the earth, intimately and graciously, and longs for his will to be done.[25] So, as you go about your business today, be conscious of heaven and on the lookout for angels.

For reflection

> **Our Father in heaven,**
> **hallowed by your name.**
> **Your kingdom come.**
> **Your will be done,**
> **on earth as it is in heaven.**
> MATTHEW 6:9–10

19 December

Glory

Glory to God...
LUKE 2:14

Glory seems a very pious word. It belongs to the world of majestic cathedrals, aromatic incense, candle wax and gold-edged Bibles. It's not an everyday word, and perhaps that's the point. It is out of the ordinary, pointing to something that is exceptional and sacred. If we don't use it, the Bible certainly does. If you care to look, you'll find it around 300 times in our English Bibles, depending on the translation. This single word is another keyhole we look through onto a wide vista of God.

When the lone angel first broke open the skies Luke tells us 'the glory of the Lord shone around them' (Luke 2:9). There are three things to grasp about this.

First, glory is a description of God himself. He is the 'king of glory' (Psalm 24:8–10) who is marked by 'splendour, beauty, magnificence, radiance'[26] and transcendence. God's glory is manifest in particular places indicating his presence. His glory appeared in the wilderness (Exodus 16:10), on the mountain (Exodus 24:16–17), in the sky (Psalm 8:1; 19:1) and, most of all, it filled the temple (1 Kings 8:10–11; 2 Chronicles 5:13–14). God's glory is variously associated with fire, light, thunder and thick cloud, all of which suggest that he is a mystery that no human mind can fully understand and he is to be approached with caution. When people encounter God's glory, they are filled with awe and react with fear at his majestic presence.

Israel's God is no petty deity or tribal idol, but the living sovereign Lord who presides magnificently over all creation.

Second, this glory is astonishingly associated with the birth of a baby. Gone is the thunder, lightning, cloud and fire of former times. Incredibly, God's glory is now linked to the arrival of a crying infant who is totally dependent on others. As Philip Yancey has written, 'The God who roared, who could order armies and empires about like pawns on a chessboard, this God emerged in Palestine as a baby who could not speak or eat solid food or control his bladder, who depended on a teenage couple for shelter, food and love.'[27] The angel armies who were used to singing songs of military victories are now found cooing over a baby's cot.

As the child grew and became a man, so the people saw God's glory in him: 'the glory as of a father's only son, full of grace and truth' (John 1:14). That was a bold departure from how they had envisaged God displaying his glory previously. The more they tried to make sense of what they had witnessed, the more they saw the glory of God in him. A few of his disciples got a glimpse of the reality behind the human life as he was transfigured before them. Significantly, since mountains had always been associated with revelations of God's glory, this took place on a high mountain, where 'his clothes became dazzling white, such as no one on earth could bleach them' (Mark 9:2–4). When he rode into Jerusalem to be greeted by the crowds as the expected Messiah, they echoed the angel's song, crying:

> Blessed is the king
>   who comes in the name of the Lord!
> Peace in heaven
>   and glory in the highest heaven!
> LUKE 19:38

To most, the cross would have been a place of shame and disgrace, but John saw it as the greatest manifestation of God's glory (John

7:39, 12:23; 17:4–5). Jesus' resurrection and exaltation were further, more obvious, steps on his path of glory (Luke 24:26, Romans 6:4). What follows next is the return of '"the Son of Man coming in a cloud" with power and great glory' (Luke 21:27). From his birth, through his life, death, resurrection and exaltation, to his coming again, Jesus is the glory of God in human form.

Third, we should note that what the angels at Bethlehem are doing is to attribute glory to God as an act of praise. Their praise does not maintain the glory of God, as if it would drain away unless topped up by his servants. It simply expresses what they know of God. His glory is an objective description of what they recognise about him, used as a word of adoration. In doing this, they stand in the long tradition of Israel where 'heavenly beings' were encouraged to 'ascribe to the Lord glory and strength... Ascribe to the Lord the glory of his name' (Psalm 29:1–2). Such praise was not the province of heavenly beings alone, since all people are invited to 'Make a joyful noise to God... sing the glory of his name; give to him glorious praise' (Psalm 66:1–2; compare 96:8).

The best response we can make is to join the choir of angels singing.

Worship the Lord in the beauty of holiness.
Bow down before Him, His glory proclaim;
Gold of obedience and incense of lowliness
Bring and adore Him; the Lord is His name!
J.S.B. Monsell, 1811–1875

For reflection

They shall sing of the ways of the Lord,
for great is the glory of the Lord.
For though the Lord is high, he regards the lowly...
PSALM 138:5–6

20 December

Heaven

Glory to God in the highest heaven...
LUKE 2:14

In my childhood there was a popular TV programme called *The Invisible Man*. Today's Advent thought might be said to be based on an invisible word! The word 'heaven' doesn't actually occur in Luke's original writing, where he simply writes, 'Glory to God in the highest'. That doesn't mean to say it's wrong. Heaven is exactly what the angels meant when they referred to 'the highest', and adding it helps to explain that to readers who may not be familiar with the background. We put heaven on our agenda when we were thinking about angels a couple of days ago. Here we explore it more fully.

Today, cosmologists often present us with mind-blowing views of the ever-expanding universe and point out what a tiny and insignificant speck planet earth really is. I, for one, am overawed with the breathtaking universe we belong to and can hardly get my mind around the simplest detail of the complex picture that is advanced, and is advancing all the time. Our Jewish forebears lived in pre-scientific days and so had a much simpler view of the universe. They spoke as if the earth was sandwiched between the heavens above and the waters below (Exodus 20:4). It was a perfectly sensible conclusion to draw from what they observed. Thinking in literal, spatial terms, heaven came to be 'up there' and so God, and his messengers, 'come down' when they visit plant earth.

Before we condemn this as all very naive, remember that we always have to express inexpressible things about God in limited human language. It is the only way we can speak of him. The alternative is not to say anything about him. Furthermore, it is wise to exercise some degree of humility about the way we speak of our universe today, because scientific advances are always correcting the assured results of yesterday's research and because language, in any case, is a living, not static, means of communication.

A solid, unchangeable core of belief about heaven can be traced throughout scripture. Heaven is above all the dwelling place of God, the location of his throne from which he rules the world. He is 'the God of heaven' (Genesis 24:7) and sits 'enthroned' above the earth (Psalms 2:4; 99:1; 123:1), surrounded by his heavenly court and the cherubim, seraphim and angels who serve him. Isaiah (6:1–5), Ezekiel (1:1–28) and much later John (Revelation 4 and 5) were given the special privilege of a vision of the throne room, but for the most part it is sealed off from human beings because its awesome sight would be too much for them to bear.

With the passage of time, ideas developed and in some circles during the period between the two testaments, 'the number of "heavens" proliferated' but there was no agreement as to how many there were. 'Sometimes there were three, or five, or seven or even ten.'[28] Paul speaks, albeit in the third person, of an experience he had when he 'was caught up to the third heaven' (2 Corinthians 12:2).

It may be that as the angels gave exultation to God 'in the highest' there was something of this in mind. Today we might envisage it in terms of a multi-storied office building with the most important people occupying the upper levels and the boss occupying the topmost floor, so that there is no one above or in a superior position to her or him. God, then, occupies the highest reaches of heaven, however many of them there may be. He is the ultimate, without any being in a superior position to him. Truthfully, though, that is probably reading more into the phrase than was intended. It almost certainly means, more simply, that the angels are not praising God in any reserved or half-hearted way for the good news of the birth of the Messiah, but that they are praising him to the rafters.

The New Testament's teaching about heaven impacts true believers in Christ in two particular respects. First, true believers are already citizens of heaven (Philippians 3:20), and consequently they live now, here on earth, by the rules and culture of heaven, seeking at all times to do the will of God and serve him. Second, even though we are already citizens of heaven we have not yet experienced fully what that means. One day we will. It's like being an heir to the estate that will eventually come our way. In the meantime the inheritance is being kept safe for us in heaven, as an earthly inheritance may be kept safe in a bank (Ephesians 1:14, 18; 1 Peter 1:4). We feel the pull of heaven now, not because of a desire to escape earth but so we can, as it were, bring it down to earth in our daily living. We feel that future pull of heaven so we prepare ourselves in the present for living there in the new creation when at last we will receive our inheritance. That's what Paul means when he says, 'I press on towards the goal for the prize of the heavenly call of God in Christ Jesus' (Philippians 3:14).

For reflection

But our citizenship is in heaven, and it is from there that we are expecting a Saviour, the Lord Jesus Christ.
PHILIPPIANS 3:20

21 December

Earth

Glory to God in the highest heaven,
   and on earth...
LUKE 2:14

In our Sunday school we used to belt out the song Jim Reeves made popular, which began:

This world is not my home; I'm just a passing through.
My treasures are laid up, somewhere beyond the blue.
The angels beckon me from heaven's open door
And I can't feel at home in this world anymore.

Could I sing that with equal gusto today? Well, I'd sing it, but perhaps not with the same enthusiasm. The song served as a healthy corrective at a time when people were clinging to material things too tightly – 'keeping up with the Joneses' – as if that was the ultimate goal in life. It is not. The song is still necessary to teach a church that often displays indifference to the future world about its importance. Yet, as often, in correcting one mistake, perhaps it over-corrected it, as if this world was entirely unimportant and only our eternal destination mattered. That devalues the present world, downgrades creation and substitutes one distortion for another.

The song of the angels gets the balance right. Have you noticed the equilibrium in their song? Glory is counterpoised by peace; God, by people; and heaven, by earth. Having looked at heaven and seen its implications for earth, it's time to look at earth itself.

Planet earth was always significant in the mind of God. He laid its foundations and brought it into existence. He didn't do so because of any need or deficiency in himself but because he is, in his essential being, a creative, life-giving and relational God. As Genesis chapters 1–3 teach us, he made the earth good. Furthermore, it was to be the sphere in which he entered into relationship with humans, who were made in his image and 'crowned ... with glory and honour', the summit of all that he had made (Psalm 8:5). He committed the superintendence of the earth into their hands, making them his representatives and vice-regents on the planet, to steward and rule over it, as he himself would have done. When things went drastically wrong, as they did when Adam and Eve wanted to grasp at equality with God himself, the world began to degenerate. Within seven generations, it had descended into so much violence and evil that God was moved to write it off. Instead, he rescued it and gave it a new beginning through Noah and his family (Genesis 6:1—9:19).

Two things emerge from these opening chapters of earth's story. First, it matters to God. He made it to begin with and could not bring himself to destroy it. Second, it is the sphere in which human beings are called to serve God.

The history of rebellion against God may have caused doubts as to how long God would continue to consider planet earth worth supporting and rescuing. There were periods when, to human eyes, God seemed to have stood back and let it go its own way. Was it worth saving? If there had ever been any doubt about it, the birth of Jesus silenced them in the most emphatic way. The significance God invested in the creation of planet earth was underlined in a mega way when he sent his only Son to visit it and eventually sacrifice himself for it. He could have raptured righteous people, such as they were, and removed them to the safety of heaven if he had so chosen. But that would have been to bypass planet earth, making it irrelevant and worthless. Instead, he chose to send his Son to earth, as a flesh and blood human being, because he wants to rescue people so that they can serve him there.

The story is not yet over. The earth and its occupants continue to lurch between experiencing God's blessing and seeking to destroy itself. The final act still lies in the future when the baby of Bethlehem, now grown and made 'Lord and Messiah' over the whole earth (Acts 2:36), will return to complete what he has begun. At that time, the earth will be renewed and in that new creation humans will live with their God, without any disruption or alienation, and rejoice in serving him and fulfilling the creation mandate which Adam and Eve so grievously failed to accomplish. Revelation 22:1–5 brings the story of Eden in Genesis 1:26—2:25 full circle.

All this suggests that we're not to go rushing through this earth, escaping from it as rapidly as we can, but rather see it as the place to serve God here and now. We serve him, primarily, by living on earth according to his commandments; by receiving forgiveness when we fail; by proclaiming forgiveness to others; and by caring for the planet, since he is Lord over it all. Yet we know the earth is not our ultimate home, and we look for a new Jerusalem, a holy city that is to come.

The angels may come from beyond, but they emphatically rejoice in the significance of Jesus' birth for the earth.

For reflection

The earth is the Lord's and all that is in it,
  the world, and those who live in it.
PSALM 24:1

22 December

Peace

**Glory to God in the highest heaven,
    and on earth peace...**
LUKE 2:14

It was a memorable Christmas Eve. Having worked through a surfeit of carol services, as you do in ministry, I was preparing for our midnight service and the one on Christmas Day itself when I got an urgent call to visit a lady who was in great distress. I found her curled up in a foetal position barely able to communicate and clearly seeking to protect herself from any outside disturbance. We sat, we waited, we prayed and eventually she began to open up a little. She was paralysed with fear in case her ex-husband broke in and attacked her and her daughter that evening or the next day. We got them to a safe place and, in the circumstances, they enjoyed a modestly happy Christmas. As the weeks went by, with the love and support of folk in church, she uncurled from her protective stance, came to know Jesus as her Saviour and began to rebuild her life after a very acrimonious divorce. The peace that had seemed an impossibility on Christmas Eve gradually became hers.

Planet earth longs for peace more than anything. In whichever direction you look, you see conflict, disharmony, tension, fighting, anger, violence, mutual destructiveness and self-harm. If, like me, you are privileged to live in a relatively peaceful country you still can't escape the quest for peace. There's plenty of social division, racial tension, industrial unrest, family disagreement and physical abuse to prevent us from being complacent. And some folk face plenty of inner conflict and a cacophony of voices inside their heads that disturb their peace.

The angels rejoice that with the birth of Christ peace has come on earth. Jesus is the bringer of peace. There was plenty of evidence of it during his lifetime. Throughout his ministry he brought peace to those who were suffering through his working of miracles. He brought peace to those whose lives were being destroyed by demons (Mark 5:1–17; Luke 8:26–37) and sometimes concluded his conversation with those he healed by telling them to 'go in peace' (Luke 7:50; 8:48). He imposed peace on the natural world when he stilled the storm in Galilee (Mark 4:39). He instructed his disciples to be peacemakers (Matthew 5:9) and frequently greeted them with words of peace, especially after his resurrection (Luke 24:36; John 20:19, 21).

Once again, looking through the keyhole, this single word 'peace' opens up an amazingly rich sight which stretches from a long time past to a future yet to come.[29] Looking in one direction we see that the Hebrew word for peace – *shalom* – is a big word, meaning far more than a lack of conflict. It points to positive, all-round well-being. David Atkinson wrote:

> Shalom is rather the absence of disorder at all levels of life and relationship. Shalom includes everything God gives for human beings in all areas of life. It means well-being in the widest sense of the word.
> Peace, then, is about being in right relationship, but it is more even than that. 'Peace' at its highest is about the enjoyment and satisfaction of being in right relationship – with God, with neighbour, with oneself, with one's environment.[30]

The foundation for peace in any arena of life is first and foremost peace with God, which is why so much stress is put on the sacrifices in the Old Testament, including the peace offering, that repair broken relationships with him and restore peace (Leviticus 1:1—7:38).

The biblical vision of peace encompasses individuals and nations, the past and the future. Micah looks forward to the day when God:

> shall judge between many peoples,
>> and shall arbitrate between strong nations far away;
> they shall beat their swords into ploughshares,
>> and their spears into pruning-hooks;
> nation shall not lift up sword against nation,
>> neither shall they learn war any more;
> but they shall all sit under their own vines and under their own
>> fig trees,
>> and no one shall make them afraid;
>> for the mouth of the Lord of hosts has spoken.
>
> MICAH 4:3–4

The United Nations and various governments love the vision of the time when nations will remodel 'swords into ploughshares and... spears into pruning-hooks'. They tend to forget that this does not happen by human effort but only, as the lead-up to this visions states, as nations are taught by God and walk in his ways rather than their own.

Looking in another direction, we see that Jesus was the means by which Micah's vision was to be fulfilled. The coming of Christ brought peace to individuals but also ended the conflict between Jew and Gentile. Paul speaks of the two hitherto hostile groups of people being made 'one new humanity' by the cross of Christ. He speaks of it as an act of reconciliation and of Christ 'making peace' between them. Overall, he concludes, 'he is our peace' (Ephesians 2:11–22). The vision of peace stretches into the future and the restoration of creation itself when all things will be reconciled to God through the cross (Colossians 1:20).

No wonder the angels celebrate the birth of the prince of peace.

For reflection

For a child has been born for us,
    a son given to us;
authority rests upon his shoulders;
    and he is named
Wonderful Counsellor, Mighty God,
    Everlasting Father, Prince of Peace.

ISAIAH 9:6

23 December

Favour

**Glory to God in the highest heaven,
    and on earth peace among those whom he favours.**
LUKE 2:14

In our hard, straight-edged, objective culture, we are suspicious of favours. Politicians who appoint family members to their staff are suspect. Employers who promote a family friend to a position are unfair. Bankers who lend acquaintances money on favourable terms are corrupt. The police must operate without any whiff of discrimination. Any gifts are bribery. Business can't be done on the back of an envelope. Interests have to be declared and any conflict of interest disqualifies you from participating.

So when we hear the angels say that peace comes to those on whom God's favour rests, we're unsure. Isn't God being discriminatory? Why doesn't his peace come to all, irrespective of whether God favours them or not? Why isn't peace sprinkled like confetti at a wedding, getting everywhere?

The succinctness of the phrase 'among those whom he favours' has lead to it being translated in various ways. Traditionally it was translated as 'peace, good will toward men' (AV) as if good will explains what peace is. The RSV translates it 'among men with whom he is pleased' as if the point was that there were plenty of men with whom he was not pleased. Other older translations speak of God's favour resting on 'men of good will' as if their good will earned his favour.[31] But there is no justification for that translation.

Can we understand more exactly what the angels meant as they sang these words? The word 'favour' (*eudokias*) means 'good pleasure' or 'thinking well of'. So what the angels are celebrating is the will of God whose good pleasure it is to bring peace to people on earth. The angels are not saying that God favours some but not others. They are rejoicing that while human beings are unable to bring about peace themselves (as is patently obvious from our daily news), God is delighted to do so for them by arranging for it through the birth, and eventual life, death and resurrection, of his Son. Peace 'comes out to us,' says Calvin, from a gracious God.[32] Or, as Luke Johnson, a contemporary Catholic commentator, puts it, favour 'clearly refers not to a human quality ("good will") that generates peace, but to a disposition of God towards humans'.[33] Peace can be ours because God is favourably disposed towards his people on earth.

In all this, God is being true to himself, for God, as Israel's own history testifies, is a God of mercy and grace who abounds 'in steadfast love and faithfulness' (Exodus 34:6).

That being so, it is quite wrong to read this as an exclusive, discriminatory statement – he favours some but not others. The point is rather that because of 'the flowing forth of God's sheer loving-kindness'[34] peace is available to all on earth, not just a select group, like the Jews. 'In the birth of this child, God's mercy has fallen on the world.'[35] But, as Calvin pointed out, it 'has effect only as we receive it'[36] and consequently, although accessible to all, it is only those who put their faith in him who enter into this peace. If there is any discrimination, we're the ones doing it by rejecting the peace and grace God offers us, not him.

The renowned Victorian preacher Charles Spurgeon called this song of the angels 'The First Christmas Carol'. Spurgeon was a doctrinally robust preacher and could be a stern one, but he was also something of a romantic. When he preached on this song, after he had shared some 'instructive thoughts', he went on to share some 'emotional thoughts'. He said,

Friends, doth not this verse, this song of the angels, stir your hearts with happiness? When I read (it), and found the angels singing it, I thought to myself, 'Then if the angels ushered in this gospel's great Head with singing, ought I not to preach it with singing? And ought not my hearers to live it with singing? Ought not their hearts to be glad and their spirits to rejoice?[37]

He went on to castigate 'sombre religionists' who thought it a sin to be joyful, as today he might castigate those who always want to find fault with God and are so overwhelmed with questions and fears that they cannot rejoice. 'Why not rather anticipate,' he continued, 'the joys of heaven, and begin to sing on earth that song which you will never need to end?'[38]

The Gloria is only eleven words in the Greek, but is packed full of meaning. Five of those words – glory, heaven, earth, peace and favour – are significant keyholes we can look through to see the immense picture of God and his dealing with creation. The fulcrum point of creation's story is reached in the birth of God's Son. The climax, when there will be 'new heavens and a new earth, where righteousness is at home' (2 Peter 3:13), is yet to come. But its arrival is guaranteed because of the birth of a vulnerable, tiny baby in Bethlehem.

For reflection

Rejoice in the Lord always; again I will say, Rejoice.
PHILIPPIANS 4:4

Jesus – the light of the nations

24–30 December

The Nunc dimittis:[39] Luke 2:28–32

Simeon took him in his arms and praised God, saying,

'Master, now you are dismissing your servant in peace,
    according to your word;
for my eyes have seen your salvation,
    which you have prepared in the presence of all peoples,
a light for revelation to the Gentiles
    and for glory to your people Israel.'

24 December

Longing for salvation

Now there was a man in Jerusalem whose name was Simeon; this man was righteous and devout, looking forward to the consolation of Israel, and the Holy Spirit rested on him.
LUKE 2:25

Would anyone, I wonder, have paid much attention to an elderly man who spent time in the temple? They probably thought nothing of it. If they'd thought at all, they may have considered him somewhat eccentric or perhaps even whispered that he took his religion too seriously. The more perceptive might have noticed he seemed to nurse a heartache. More likely, they just treated him as part of the furniture. Yet he comes to play a part in the Christmas story and sings a song that has been sung for centuries, every Sunday in some church traditions. His name is Simeon.

I've buried a number of elderly people in my time who I knew only in their final years, and sometimes only in their final weeks. One of the things I quickly discovered in ministry was that those I only met as frail and towards the end of their lives sometimes had great stories to tell from the past. They had been heroes in the war, or responsible for huge achievements in education or industry, or witnesses to history. I often wish I had talked with them more to learn of their experiences.

Luke, who set out to write a carefully researched account of the life of Jesus, had tracked Simeon down as a witness to history. Simeon held the baby Jesus in his arms; he was convinced that Jesus was the Messiah.

The media often tell us about the composer or the story behind a popular song so that we gain a deeper appreciation of its words and significance. So it is with Simeon. Who was he and why should he be trusted as a reliable witness? What is curious about the way Luke introduces him is both how much he says about him and what he omits. Later tradition suggested that Simeon was a priest and the son of a famous rabbi, Hillel, and the father of Gamaliel, who cautiously defends the apostles in Acts 5:33–39. It is even suggested that he was president of the Sanhedrin one year.[40] There's scant evidence to support these suggestions and, even if true, Luke shows no interest in them. To Luke he is 'a man in Jerusalem… this man'. What Luke is interested in is his character and spirituality. He tells us a lot about that.

First, Luke tells us Simeon was 'righteous and devout'. As a righteous man he kept the commandments, living both by the great ones and the more minor ones. He was known for his clean living. As a devout man he was punctilious in his observance of his religious duties. Howard Marshall points out the word devout originally meant cautious, which, he says, is meant positively here but later dropped out of Christian use 'perhaps because of its negative tone'.[41] Being 'devout' in the sense of being cautious is something to be prized in a professional. How glad we were for a consultant who was 'devout' in his administration of his drugs and his all-round care when my wife was undergoing a difficult pregnancy. It saved our unborn child's life. The builder, the lawyer, the accountant and every other professional need to perform their duties 'devoutly' with care. Sloppiness serves no one. Should we be more casual, less cautious, careless, less attentive, in our serving God? Of course not.

Second, Luke tells us Simeon was 'looking forward to the consolation of Israel'. Like many in Israel he was thoroughly disheartened by Israel's state. Weren't they God's elect? Had not God promised someone would reign on David's throne for ever (2 Samuel 7)? Why then were they under the boot of the Romans who barely tolerated their religion? Why were the Jewish establishment trying to appease the Romans or negotiate their way through a settlement that avoided trouble?

Israel, of course, had been here before, with the Egyptians, Babylonians, Persians and Greeks, and Simeon knew the answer did not lie in rebellion but in waiting. His patient waiting was not the waiting of resignation but the eager, alert waiting of someone who knows something dramatic is going to happen. They just don't know when. For Simeon, that something dramatic was the arrival of the Messiah who would cry 'Comfort, O comfort my people' (Isaiah 40:1), announce peace (Isaiah 52:7–10), bring an end to suffering and usher in the new age. Furthermore, God had promised this old man Simeon that he wouldn't die before he had seen the Messiah for himself.

Then one day he felt compelled to go to the temple and perceived that a baby, brought by a young couple to observe the rite of purification, was the answer to his waiting. The Messiah had come. Simeon's faithful trust in God had been rewarded by God's faithful fulfilment of his promise. His people were about to be comforted.

For reflection

I wait for the Lord, my soul waits,
  and in his word I hope;
my soul waits for the Lord
  more than those who watch for the morning.
  more than those who watch for the morning.

PSALM 130:5–6

25 December

The arrival of salvation

**Master now you are dismissing your servant in peace,
    according to your word;
for my eyes have seen your salvation.**
LUKE 2:29–30

Do you remember the sense of keen anticipation you felt as a young child waiting for Christmas Day? The presents had been wrapped for some time and proved a tantalising provocation under the tree. The mince pies, milk (or something stronger) and a carrot had been put out for Father Christmas and Rudolph. You were put to bed and told that the sooner you went to sleep, the sooner it would be Christmas Day. But excitement levels were so high that sleep was the last thing on your mind. Eventually, you did drop off, only to wake early in the morning to find your stocking filled. The day had arrived!

I'm not suggesting that Simeon sustained that level of keen anticipation for decades, or even years. But his spiritual senses were alert and had been finely tuned for a long time before that special day when he went into the temple. When he took the baby Jesus in his arms he knew the day he had anticipated for so long had at last arrived. In some ways, the most important word in today's text is 'now'. 'Now' is placed in a prominent position as the first word in his song.[44] It echoes the message of the angel 'to you is born *this day*… a Saviour who is the Messiah, the Lord' (Luke 2:11, emphasis added).

Salvation has arrived. Everything is about to change. The world will never be the same again. God's compassion and grace was to be available; his forgiveness, releasing people from their sins, would flow; *shalom*, peace, would be forthcoming for anyone; and, a new, deep kind of freedom obtainable for all people. It wasn't just another day, but 'the day of salvation' (2 Corinthians 6:2). All that would be required for this salvation to be experienced was that people trusted the Saviour and became his disciples.

Somewhat paradoxically, though, this salvation had come in the form of a baby whose parents must have been pretty poor, since they presented the type of offering reserved for those who could not afford much (Luke 2:24). It's not how we nor many people in Simeon's day would have envisaged salvation arriving. But because of his long-standing and deep spirituality, Simeon had insight given to him by the Holy Spirit that this little bundle in his arms was indeed the Messiah. Why, his very name, Jesus, pointed to the fact that he would be the rescuer and deliverer of Israel.

The good news of salvation for Israel was bad news for Simeon. God had made it clear that the Messiah's arrival would coincide with his own departure from the scene. Simeon doesn't seem to view it as bad news, though. His words exude trust and hope-filled surrender. His choice of words belongs to the world of the household. He sees himself as a servant speaking to his master, who dismisses him from his duty. That sounds harsh. But that's to miss the point. The 'dismissal' is not in any way unkind or insensitive. Rather, it conjures up the picture of a servant having done his job well, receiving his reward by being set free, and released from ongoing slavery, duty and obligation. Simeon, having served loyally by waiting to identify the Messiah, is now released from his responsibility and free to enjoy his rest in the fuller presence of God.

He's saying something rather similar to Paul, who wrote, 'For to me, living is Christ and dying is gain.' Life here, said Paul, is 'fruitful labour', but 'to depart and be with Christ... is far better' (Philippians 1:21–23). I can hear Simeon mouthing a gentle yet confident 'Amen' to that.

Simeon demonstrates a true 'Christian' attitude to death. It is a departure and a release into a fuller life, in the light of the arrival of the Saviour who, through his own death, defeated our ultimate enemy and released us from fear of it. How different that is to the way many in contemporary society consider death: they spend time denying it rather than preparing for it. As Billy Graham once said, 'Though Christians have no immunity from death, death is to them a friend rather than a foe, the beginning rather than the end.'[45] Simeon had now completed his term of service and could depart this life with the assurance that salvation had come.

Our family has often rejoiced that, 'The day has arrived'. Sometimes it was a graduation, sometimes a new job, sometimes a wedding, sometimes a house move, sometimes a holiday, sometimes a retirement. But Christmas Day, the day about which Simeon said, 'the day has come at last', outclasses them all.

For reflection

> **As we work together with him, we urge you also not to accept the grace of God in vain. For he says,**
> **'At an acceptable time I have listened to you,**
> **and on a day of salvation I have helped you.'**
> **See, now is the acceptable time; see, now is the day of salvation!**
> 2 CORINTHIANS 6:1–2

26 December

Witness to salvation

It had been revealed to him by the Holy Spirit that he would not see death before he had seen the Lord's Messiah. Guided by the Spirit, Simeon came into the temple; and when the parent brought in the child Jesus, to do for him what was customary under the law, Simeon took him in his arms and praised God...

LUKE 2:26–28

The BBC reporter John Simpson has been a witness to the most momentous events of our age. He has accompanied the Ayatollah Khomeini back to Iran, seen the Tianamen Square protests of 1989, the downfall of communism later that year, the release of Nelson Mandela and the subsequent Gulf War, and has entered Afghanistan, famously disguised in a burqa. On each occasion it was obvious that something earth-shaking was happening. The birth of Jesus was also earth-shaking, but not nearly as obvious as the events Simpson had witnessed. What was it that made Simeon make the declaration we considered yesterday: 'my eyes have seen your salvation'? How did Simeon know that he was holding the Messiah in his arms? One baby, surely, is much like another!

Luke is obviously aware of the difficulty. Consequently, he mentions the part the Holy Spirit played in it all, not once, or even twice, but three times. Simeon's devout life meant 'the Holy Spirit rested on him' in a comprehensive and general sense, as a permanent presence. But then the Holy Spirit 'revealed to him' a particular promise 'that he would not see death before he had seen the Lord's

Messiah'. Even more specifically, on one particular day, 'Guided by the Spirit, (he) came into the temple', and that was the day when Mary and Joseph brought Jesus into the temple precincts, almost certainly into the Court of Women. The Spirit not only prompted Simeon to go to the temple that day but also enabled Simeon to recognise the child as the Messiah,[42] something the high priest, whose job it was to identify the Messiah, later failed to do (John 11:49–53). According to Luke, then, the Holy Spirit moves from the general, to the particular, to the even more specific in Simeon's life. All the time, the Spirit's revelation sharpens in focus.

Mention of the Holy Spirit like this puts Simeon on a par with the Old Testament prophets, as well as anticipating the experience later Christians would have of the Holy Spirit. The prophets were the ones on whom the Holy Spirit came, charismatically revealing God's words and giving them messages of truth to pass on to others. Simeon caps their expectations about the coming Messiah, identifying, under inspiration, that Jesus is he.

The lead-in to this cameo about Simeon also says something significant. Mary and Joseph went to the temple 'for their purification according to the law of Moses' (Luke 2:22; see Leviticus 12). Luke seems deliberately to be drawing attention to the way in which the law and prophets combine in their witness to Jesus as the Messiah.[43] The most significant voices in the Jewish faith reinforce each other and blend to point to Jesus as the fulfilment of all their longings and aspirations.

How do we know that Simeon's 'prophecy' is not simply the ramblings of an old man who, over-excited and determined to see his pent-up wishes somehow fulfilled before he dies, one day becomes fixated on a young couple's baby and declares him to be the Messiah?

First, there is no evidence that Simeon spoke under ecstatic inspiration, as if he was no longer in control of his mind. The Spirit's revelation occurred through a thoughtful inward sense-impression rather than because he was in a trance or intoxicated by something. He seems in full possession of his faculties.

Second, and more importantly, there was a simple test to prove whether prophets were speaking the truth or speaking falsehood and by implication voicing their own dreams. Israel had had plenty of experience of the latter and had frequently been misled by lying prophets, as Ezekiel 13 testifies. The question, quite simply, was, did their prophecies come true or not? Deuteronomy 18:22 said, 'If a prophet speaks in the name of the Lord but the thing does not take place or prove true, it is a word that the Lord has not spoken.' Conversely, Jeremiah 28:9 stipulated, 'when the word of [the] prophet comes true, then it will be known that the Lord has truly sent the prophet.' You only have to look at what happened to Jesus to know that Simeon's prophecy about this baby was true.

While we know little of Simeon, we can be sure that he was a true witness to history and a true witness to salvation.

For reflection

We declare to you what was from the beginning, what we have heard, what we have seen with our own eyes, what we have looked at and touched with our hands, concerning the word of life – this life was revealed, and we have seen it and testify to it, and declare to you the eternal life that was with the Father and was revealed to us.

1 JOHN 1:1–2

27 December

The transparency of salvation

… which you have prepared in the presence of all peoples.
LUKE 2:31

Compared to the loud bursts of praise heard in the songs of Mary, Zechariah and the angels, Simeon's song adopts a quieter, more reflective style. Their songs were upbeat in style, using the major musical keys. Simeon's song is softer and contemplative, conveying the same music in gentler, minor keys. To change the metaphor, their songs were painted in the bright colours of summer, his is coloured with quieter hues. It is by no means limited to his own interior musings, as we shall see, but it comes from the depths of a seasoned, steady, wise man who is now contemplating his own death.

Buried within the deceptively simple single line of Simeon's song that we contemplate today are a number of dualities. Simeon's private moment with the child Jesus had a long, public preparation. Imagine the scene. Old pastor Simeon comes across a young couple and spends some intimate moments with them congratulating them on their new arrival and praying God's blessing on him. But then he goes much further and, praising God, identifies the child as the Saviour of the world. The court of women would have been a crowded place. Women would have been offering their prayers, other couples could have been coming and going and priests would have been performing their rituals. Yet for Simeon, and Mary and Joseph, this was an intensely private moment. Would anyone have noticed their body language? Would anyone have eavesdropped on their conversation? I doubt it. It was a busy, bustling place.

Yet this private conversation didn't take place 'out of the blue', unprepared. The apparent spontaneity belied the fact that centuries of preparation had led up to it. Mark Twain remarked, 'Impromptu speaking... That is a difficult thing. I used to begin about a week ahead, and write out my impromptu speech and get it by heart.'[46] Simeon's 'impromptu' speech had been in preparation much, much longer than that. The preparation had begun centuries before, while throughout his lifetime he had been groomed, as it were, for this moment together with Mary, Joseph and even Jesus. They were playing their personal roles in fulfilment of public promises made through the prophets over many years that 'the glory of the Lord shall be revealed, and all people shall see it together' (Isaiah 40:5).

While the moment may have been private, God was not acting in secret, as those prophecies showed. Some years later, Paul drew attention to the same feature of the way God works when replying to Festus, not now about the incarnation but about the resurrection of Jesus. He said of King Agrippa, 'I am certain that none of these things has escaped his notice, for this was not done in a corner. King Agrippa, do you believe the prophets? I know that you believe' (Acts 26:26–27). Christianity is not about secret knowledge that only a special few can access but about events prepared and enacted in the open for all to see.

So private and public good news, past and present events, function in partnership with each other. There is also another partnership hidden in Simeon's song, that between a personal faith and a public claim.

Simeon's song is immensely personal. He gives voice to his personal testimony to Jesus, born of long years of devotion and set alight now by the Holy Spirit's inspiration. His own eyes have led him to this conclusion; his experience has led him to affirm his faith. Simeon literally stakes his own life on it. If this is the Saviour, as he claims, then he is about to die, even if he will die a happy man, 'in peace', having seen all his life's ambitions fulfilled.

Simeon's personal testimony, however, doesn't remain a privatised affair. He claims that this Saviour will play a public role and have implications for 'all peoples'. Some people regard faith as so intensely private that they never speak of it to others. Some people believe that faith is about their personal salvation, so they draw a boundary around themselves and think it has nothing to do with the public square in which the affairs of economics, politics, business and education are played out. Simeon would beg to differ. The birth of this child affects the whole world. As the American evangelical Jim Wallis recently argued, 'Salvation involves personal transformation, but it doesn't stop there.'[47]

Simeon teaches that the truth about Jesus Christ is not just a truth for Christians but also a truth for all, whatever their nationality, ethnicity, cultural background or religious history. Simeon implies that to collude with the pluralist lie – that Jesus may be a wonderful Saviour if you believe in him, but that others can find different routes to knowing God and experiencing salvation – is a delusion. Jesus' coming was 'prepared in the presence of all peoples'. The claim about him is global in its reach. Simeon's Saviour is not about saving a few souls but about impacting the whole of God's world, the cultural as well as geographical world, so that it can be rescued from its present path of destruction.

The gospel, as Bishop Lesslie Newbiggen sought to teach the Western church in recent years, is 'public truth', not private, still less subjectivized, faith.[48] Simeon felt the message of salvation personally and deeply, but he was also convinced it was a message for 'all peoples'.

For reflection

This was not done in a corner.
ACTS 26:26

28 December

The scope of salvation

... a light for revelation to the Gentiles
and for glory to your people Israel.
LUKE 2:32

The trouble with looking through keyholes is that what you see may surprise you. You can't always be sure of what's on the other side. Looking through the keyhole of Simeon's song, our eyes are immediately struck by the appearance of Gentiles in the scene. How did they get in? What are they doing there? Who invited them?

As Simeon's song reaches its climax he explains more fully who the 'all peoples' he's referred to are. His world was basically divided into two camps, with a great chasm fixed between them. There were Jews and there were Gentiles. The Jews were God's chosen people who enjoyed the special privileges of the law, the temple and all the other things that came with the covenant. The Gentiles were... well, just the rest. They were godless aliens, unclean, no-hopers, outsiders who were far from God, morally insensitive with befuddled minds or, to quote Paul, 'darkened in their understanding' (Ephesians 2:11–13; 4:18–19). Now, Simeon claims, the chasm has been repaired and Jesus' salvation includes Gentiles as well as the Jews.

Jesus' coming means light instead of darkness for the Gentiles. Having just mentioned how Paul saw the Gentiles without Christ, we can readily understand why they would have needed enlightening. Darkness clouded their minds and their morals. Darkness prevented them from seeing God. They stumbled through life out of touch with their creator, clutching at all sorts of religious straws that could not save them. They needed enlightening.

The image of light was no accident. It had a long history in the sacred books of Israel. The prophet Isaiah had foreseen a future age when Israel would fulfil her covenant calling and be a light to the nations (Isaiah 42:6–7). God would give Israel 'as a light to the nations, that my salvation may reach the end of the earth' (Isaiah 49:6). Now Simeon proclaims those prophecies had reached their fulfilment.

God's plan to bless all nations through Israel was anything but a late invention by Isaiah. From the beginning, God, whose first words were, 'Let there be light' (Genesis 1:3), had chosen Abraham's family as the channel through which 'all the families of the earth shall be blessed' (Genesis 12:3). Too often, they'd forgotten their commission and even betrayed and twisted it into something intended purely for their own national benefit. As far as God was concerned, that was never the purpose of their election. Now, at last, with Christ's coming, the global embrace of God's grace would become a reality.

Some have queried whether Simeon's words really do indicate that Gentiles will experience God's salvation or whether they stop short of that. 'A light for revelation' may mean simply that their blinkers are taken off and they see things as they really are, but not necessarily that they act on it or are saved by it. Could it not add to their misery? They see what they're missing but are condemned not to benefit from it? That can't be so. Zechariah's song has already spoken of the light (see 17 December), where it clearly means it brings salvation. As Joel Green says, 'Through God's agent of salvation, people do not merely see the evidence of advent of God's dominion, they are engulfed in it; they are, as it were, led from the dominion of darkness into the light.'[49] Jesus is not just a light to Israel, but the light of the nations too.

If Jesus' coming means light instead of darkness for Gentiles it means glory instead of shame for Israel. Ancient cultures revolved around issues of glory and shame. To be insulted by others, defeated in war or under the thumb of a foreign power was all a matter of shame. Israel longed for its glory to be restored; the glory it had known in the days of David and Solomon. Simeon rejoiced that its glory was about to be restored by Jesus. True, the music of glory was to be transposed into an unexpected key. Their shame had been caused by their own sin rather than by stronger political powers occupying them. The first step to restoring glory, then, was repentance. Glory was no longer tied to a piece of land or measured by material wealth. Glory was to spread around the world bringing people of all nations, not just Jews, to experience the mercy and grace of God. Israel's honour would be restored, but not in the way they expected.

The scope of salvation is universal. Gentile and Jew are included. In Simeon's day the inclusion of Gentiles may have been the surprise. In our world, the balance has shifted and many take it for granted that Christians will mainly be Gentiles. But God still has a plan for Israel, as Paul explains in Romans 9—11. That's because the salvation of Jesus is genuinely offered to all, Jew and Gentile, Gentile and Jew alike.

For reflection

For there is no distinction between Jew and Greek; the same Lord is Lord of all and is generous to all who call on him. For, 'Everyone who calls on the name of the Lord shall be saved.'
ROMANS 10:12–13

29 December

The cost of salvation

This child is destined for the falling and the rising of many in Israel… and a sword will pierce your own soul too.
LUKE 2:34–35

From the moment Prince William was born, he was destined one day to be king. Few babies are born with such a sense of destiny. Parents nurse them in their arms, amazed at the miracle of the potential locked up in such a tiny lump of crying, human flesh, but wondering what will become of them when they grow up. Prince William's future was already laid down for him. So, too, was the future of baby Jesus. If ever there was a man of destiny, it was him.

When he had finished his astonishing song, Simeon turned to Mary in private conversation. Joseph was present, but Simeon fixed his attention on Mary because the things he had to say especially involved her.[50] Their heads were already spinning at what they had heard and the conversation did nothing to calm them down. Jesus, Simeon said, had been 'appointed'.

'Appointed' is perhaps a better translation than 'destined'. We say Jack was destined to be a doctor because his parents were doctors, or Mary was destined to go into politics because she came from a political dynasty. We don't mean they had no choice but that in all probability they'd end up doing this or that because of their upbringing. If that's all that was meant, Jesus would have ended up as a carpenter!

But Jesus had been chosen for a particular mission even before he was born and the course of his life had been laid down for him; a life that would end on a cross. Fulfilling his destiny would involve 'many in Israel' but would also have a particular impact on his mother.

This child would determine the future standing of many in Israel, claims Simeon. He doesn't spell out how, but is probably hinting that people's reactions to Jesus would determine their own destinies. God would bless those who trusted and followed him. Equally, God would reject those who rejected and despised him, no matter what their position or title in Israel's political or religious pecking order. As John later explained, the honour of God and the honour of Jesus were inseparable: 'Anyone who does not honour the Son does not honour the Father who sent him' (John 5:23). Jesus was certainly a divisive figure. Not all welcomed him or bought into his message. Some thought him delusional or even dangerous and not only spoke against him but actively opposed him to the point of arranging his execution.

Again, it's only a hint. But when Simeon spoke like this he possibly had the picture of a stone in his mind which crops up a couple of times in the Old Testament. Psalm 118:22 speaks of a stone that builders rejected as useless becoming the most significant block in a new building. Isaiah 8:14 also uses the image of a stone but points out that stones are obstacles we stub our toes on or stumble over, causing us pain or to fall down. Peter (1 Peter 2:7–8) and Paul (Romans 9:33) came to see that these texts pointed to Jesus. Had they taken their cue from Simeon? What people really thought of Jesus, the man of destiny, determined their destiny with God, as it still does. And there would be no use pretending, for he, as we saw in Mary's song, would reveal what people really thought in the recesses of their minds. So the truth would out.

Then Simeon changes the lens from a wide-angle to a close-up one focused on Mary. Jesus' great destiny with its implications 'for many', also had implications for her, and they would be painful: 'a sword would pierce your own soul too'. Mary would see her beloved son ridiculed and opposed throughout his life, before being rejected, arrested, falsely tried, abused and then shamefully put to death. What would any mother feel, let alone a mother who had been promised great things about her son by an angel, and the mother of a son who had led the most honest, loving and grace-filled life that had ever been? She would nurse the insecurity throughout his life and carry the pain deep within her own life right to his cross.

Rescues are usually costly affairs. The firefighter goes into the fire, the lifeboat crew is winched into the sea and the soldier suffers enemy fire to get his or her colleagues out of danger.[51] Rescuing people from sin, Satan and death was certainly costly. Salvation was only possible because Christ went into the fire of sin, entered the sea of death and underwent enemy fire, at the cost of his own life. His was the ultimate cost. But we should not forget that Mary also bore the cost of seeing all this played out before her very eyes in the life of her very much-loved son. Such is the cost of salvation.

For reflection

He himself bore our sins in his body on the cross, so that, free from sins, we might live for righteousness; by his wounds you have been healed.
1 PETER 2:24

30 December

Confirmation of salvation

There was also a prophet, Anna...
LUKE 2:36

Thank God for Miss Seker. In all honesty I can't tell you much about her. She was an old lady – in reality, probably about 50 – in the church of my youth. I've no idea of her background. She was just there. She probably had had little education and certainly wasn't in an impressive job, but she was known for her prayer life and complete devotion to Jesus Christ. On one occasion when I was a teenager, I had preached a mini-sermon at some event and she wrote me a note the next day. I wish I still had it, but it has been lost over the years. It was full of encouragement but pointed out to me that I had not read the passage of scripture carefully enough and so had missed an important detail and had preached a shallow gospel as a result. She was right. How grateful I am to her.

When I picture Anna, I think of Miss Seker, although we know a little more about Luke's Anna than I know about the 'Anna' of my youth. Luke introduces her as 'a prophet', not, note, a prophetess. True, she was a successor to Miriam, Deborah and Huldah but she was equally a successor to Isaiah, Ezekiel and Zechariah. Her father's name was Phanuel, although we know nothing more about him than his name. What is significant is that she came from the unimportant tribe of Asher. Asher had been dispersed after the exile but, unusually, Anna had made her way to Jerusalem. She didn't really belong there, among the religious establishment. She came from the margins of the nation and represented those who didn't quite fit. At 84, she was old and had been a widow most of her life, since she was only married for seven years. Like Miss Seker, who always seemed to be there when the church doors opened, she was devoted to the faith and 'never left the temple', where she exercised a remarkable life of prayer and fasting. To many, she would have seemed an unimportant, insignificant old woman and nothing more.

She was important to God, however, and he rewarded her long devotion to him on the day when Mary and Joseph came to the temple with Jesus. We puzzle, as we did with Simeon, how it could be that she identified this couple and this child as the answer to Jerusalem's longing for redemption. Yet, like Simeon, she did. It could only be that her closeness to God and her prophetic gift, honed over the years, led her to be sensitive to the Holy Spirit's prompting. Like everyone else in the Christmas story, once she had made the identification, she burst into songs of praise. Sadly, her words are not recorded but she probably used some of the ancient songs of Israel found in the psalms to express her joy that the Messiah had arrived. Oh, and she did more than sing. She chatted: she began 'to speak about the child to all who were looking for the redemption of Jerusalem'. You can image it, can't you? An elderly lady you couldn't shut up!

How wonderful that Anna gets this walk-on part in the Christmas story. It's typical of Luke to include her. Throughout his Gospel he is concerned to balance male with female participants in the life of Jesus and also to tell stories that come both from the man's and the woman's world of the day.[52] To use an obvious example, he tells a story of a lost coin in the home and then a story about a lost sheep in the fields (Luke 15:1–10). Having introduced Simeon, a male witness to Jesus as the Messiah, Luke would have been keen to call upon a female witness to the same truth. Hence, Anna is called to the witness box. She's not just there as a counterpart to Simeon but as a witness in her own right, with her own story to tell and her own convictions to share.

There is another reason, too, why Luke calls on Anna as a witness. If we have any clue about Simeon's background, we're right to conclude he was part of the religious establishment, from the top drawer of Jewish society. Anna was 'a nobody', from the margins. As far as we know, she never held office and didn't come from the right sort of family. As a prophet she would have established her credibility by exercising a personal, charismatic gift, not because she'd graduated from rabbi school or had the right parents. She represents the outsiders. Standing alongside Simeon, their combined witness confirms the appeal of Jesus to all, men and women alike, insider and outsider equally, socially significant and socially insignificant, and Gentile as much as Jew. Jesus truly is the light of the nations.

Thank God for Anna, the godly, chatty witness to Jesus. And thank God for Miss Seker, who centuries later stood in her shoes.

For reflection

> But God chose what is foolish in the world to shame the wise; God chose what is weak in the world to shame the strong; God chose what is low and despised in the world... so that no one might boast in the presence of God.
> 1 CORINTHIANS 1:27–29

Jesus – the splendour of creation

31 December–6 January

The songs of John, Paul and Hebrews

In this final week we look through some different keyholes to those that Luke provides. New keyholes mean new vistas, new insights. The songs that Luke records look forwards to what Jesus will accomplish. The 'songs' we now look at were composed after Jesus' life on earth and look back. If the earlier songs express hope, these later songs express confidence that the hope has been realised. The earlier songs claim Jesus has significance for needy persons and powerful nations; these magnify his significance and claim he has import for all creation.

In the beginning was the Word, and the Word was with God, and the Word was God. He was in the beginning with God. All things came into being through him, and without him not one thing came into being. What has come into being in him was life, and the life was the light of all people. The light shines in the darkness, and the darkness did not overcome it.

There was a man sent from God, whose name was John. He came as a witness to testify to the light, so that all might believe through him. He himself was not the light, but he came to testify to the light. The true light, which enlightens everyone, was coming into the world.

He was in the world, and the world came into being through him; yet the world did not know him. He came to what was his own, and his own people did not accept him. But to all who received him, who believed in his name, he gave power to become children of God, who were born, not of blood or of the will of the flesh or of the will of man, but of God.

And the Word became flesh and lived among us, and we have seen his glory, the glory as of a father's only son, full of grace and truth. (John testified to him and cried out, 'This was he of whom I said, "He who comes after me ranks ahead of me because he was before me."') From his fullness we have all received, grace upon grace. The law indeed was given through Moses; grace and truth came through Jesus Christ. No one has ever seen God. It is God the only Son, who is close to the Father's heart, who has made him known.

JOHN 1:1–18

He is the image of the invisible God, the firstborn of all creation; for in him all things in heaven and on earth were created, things visible and invisible, whether thrones or dominions or rulers or powers – all things have been created through him and for him. He himself is before all things, and in him all things hold together. He is the head of the body, the church; he is the beginning, the firstborn from the dead, so that he might come to have first place in everything. For in him all the fullness of God was pleased to dwell, and through him God was pleased to reconcile to himself all things, whether on earth or in heaven, by making peace through the blood of his cross.

COLOSSIANS 1:15–20

Long ago God spoke to our ancestors in many and various ways by the prophets, but in these last days he has spoken to us by a Son, whom he appointed heir of all things, through whom he also created the worlds. He is the reflection of God's glory and the exact imprint of God's very being, and he sustains all things by his powerful word. When he had made purification for sins, he sat down at the right hand of the Majesty on high, having become as much superior to angels as the name he has inherited is more excellent than theirs.

HEBREWS 1:1–4

31 December

In the beginning

In the beginning was the Word, and the Word was with God, and the Word was God. He was in the beginning with God. All things came into being through him, and without him not one thing came into being.
JOHN 1:1–3

Read John 1:1–13.

There are two ways you can look at the Himalayas. The first is to look up at them from ground level as you camp in their foothills. Alternatively, you can fly over them and see them some distance below. Both give you a true picture of the mountains, clouds permitting, but they give you two different perspectives. From below, you may see the detail and find them awe-inspiring as they tower above you, but you may not actually be able to see the top or get a true sense of their magnitude. From the air, you see the whole breathtaking picture and enter into their grandeur more fully. Flying above them gives you a better perspective.

The songs of Mary, Zechariah, the angels and Simeon have a sense of perspective. Their songs are full not of human logic but of divinely revealed truth. Even so, the songs are very close to the events and are looking at Jesus' birth, as it were, close up. When John comes to write about his birth, he finds that perspective too restricting. Stories of a young unmarried mother, a manger in Bethlehem, or shepherds being entertained by angel choirs are not sufficient for him. He needs, continuing the analogy, to get on the plane and soar high above the scene to gain a better view. When he does so, he provides us with an awesome sight of the baby of Bethlehem.

According to John, to tell the story of Jesus you can't begin at Nazareth or Bethlehem. You have to begin with creation. Consciously echoing Genesis 1, John places Jesus firmly in a unique relationship to God the creator and to the earth he created. Look at the parallels.

Both Genesis 1 and John 1 start with the words 'In the beginning'. Here is the commencement of all things on planet earth. There was nothing prior to what Genesis or John are about to unfold. Genesis soon tells us 'Then God said… ' How do we speak? By using words, of course. So it is that Jesus was the Word 'who was with God'. Words express our innermost thoughts and communicate our intentions. Speaking as humans, our words do not always achieve what we hope, but God's words never fall short. What he speaks happens. Life itself has its origins in the Word.

Life and light are inextricably linked. So, the first thing God said was 'Let there be light' (Genesis 1:3) and, John claims, that light was none other than Jesus. He 'shines in the darkness' to bring life to all. John is a superb artist with words and so gives a deeper meaning to the word 'light' than merely claiming it was essential to the creation of physical life. He's picking up from Isaiah who, as we saw, characterised people as living in darkness,[53] by which he meant the darkness of fear, sin, and alienation from God and from others. Now, in the coming of Jesus, the light has come to show people a way out of their predicament and to enlighten them as to how to live fully and freely in relationship with God.

Right from the beginning, John signals that not all would welcome the light. Some insects scuttle away to find shelter in darkness; equally some people run away to seek the protection of darkness because they enjoy living immoral lives (John 3:19). Others, far from quietly avoiding the light, oppose it vigorously and try to snuff it out, so that the darkness triumphs. They tried that supremely on the cross but they failed completely to do so as 'darkness did not overcome it.'

These are audacious, even mystical, claims to make about a human being, Jesus of Nazareth, especially that he, the Word, 'was God'. Bold though they are, that's exactly what John is claiming. This Word is not some unreal, metaphysical, unknowable, divine ideal. John grounds it all in the real human life of Jesus. While stretching one hand back to the origins of creation to explain Jesus, with the other hand John firmly grips what happened in his own lifetime. 'There was a man sent from God, whose name was John' (the Baptist). 'He,' Jesus, 'was in the world' and we saw him with our own eyes. Furthermore, he transformed people's lives, enabling them to begin life again as true children of God. Paradoxically, while John lifts off to give us the grandest view of Jesus, his feet never leave the ground.

The almighty, creator God entered our world a vulnerable, fragile baby who breathed his first breath and cried his first cry in Bethlehem. As Charles Wesley put it:

Let earth and heaven combine,
angels and men agree
to praise in songs divine
the incarnate Deity,
our God contracted to a span,
incomprehensibly made man.
Charles Wesley, 1704–1788

For reflection

For the word of the Lord is upright
　and all his work is done in faithfulness…
By the word of the Lord the heavens were made,
　and all their host by the breath of his mouth.
PSALM 33:4, 6

1 January

The embodied Word

And the Word became flesh and lived among us, and we have seen his glory, the glory as of a father's only son, full of grace and truth.
JOHN 1:14

Read John 1:14–18.

I'm never sure whether to be flattered or irritated when students interrupt my lecture and ask me to repeat my last sentence because they want to get every carefully crafted clause down accurately. I feel flattered that I've said something they think worth repeating. I feel irritated because when a student is concerned to get every word down they're usually displaying their insecurity rather than engaging with the substance of my teaching. Moreover, since I lecture from notes, not a script, 30 seconds later I often can't remember exactly how I put it!

There are times, though, when every word does count and they're worth mulling over carefully. That's certainly true of John 1:14. It's like a rich, gourmet meal where every flavoursome morsel is to be chewed over at leisure. To help us digest the richness of John's meal, let me draw attention to five different items on the plate

First, he tells us *what the Word did*: he 'became flesh'. The Word who was God 'was' from the beginning, prior to creation itself, but then he 'became' a human being. Life didn't start when the Word was born at Bethlehem. Rather he took on a new status then and became something he had not been before – embodied. Paul says the same thing: Christ 'was in the form of God… but emptied himself… being born in human likeness' (Philippians 2:6–7). It mattered that he was fully and truly human or else he would not even have been able to identify with the humanity he sought to rescue, let alone actually save them.

Second, John tells us *where the Word came*: 'and lived among us'. The gods of the ancient world condescended occasionally to put in brief guest appearances on earth but they were never 'real', even to their devotees. By contrast, Jesus not only lived on earth as a genuine human but also came to stop for a good time. He 'moved into the neighborhood'.[54] This meant that people could easily check him out and unmask him if he wasn't who he claimed to be. His family, his disciples and the crowds knew him well and knew him to be authentic. His enemies could only successfully conspire against him by lying, as later events were to testify. John's word for 'lived among us' is 'tabernacled', a word which had particular associations. In other words, just as God had lived among his people at the centre of their wilderness camp in the tabernacle, so now God himself in the person of Jesus had come to take up residence again among his people.

Third, John tells us *what the Word displayed*: 'glory'. God's glory once shone from Mount Sinai, and out from the tabernacle and later the temple. Now the majestic, transcendent splendour of God shines out from Jesus. They may not always have seen it that way because his glory was 'full of grace and truth'. They expected God's glory to manifest itself in powerful justice and the rigid application of the law, which punished wrongdoers, not in a manifestation of genuine grace. They'd become so distorted in their thinking and believed so many of the devil's lies it was hard to accept that Jesus' counter-cultural message was the truth. But it was. The law went back to Moses but Jesus now came to demonstrate and fulfil its true intent, which had become obscured by petty interpretation and tradition.

Fourth, John reminds us *who the Word was*: 'a father's only son'. At the opening of his Gospel, John set out the unique relationship between the human Jesus and the eternal God. The Word was 'with God' and, indeed, 'was God' (v. 1). Now recast in terms of sonship, John tells us that as a son Jesus stands in a unique relationship with the Father. All human beings are sons and daughters of God but their relationship as children to their father is of a different order than his being the Son of God. He is in the closest relationship of all with the Father (v. 18), giving him a unique ability to be the Saviour of the world.

Fifth, John explains *why the Word came*: 'No one has ever seen God. It is God the only Son, who is close to the Father's heart, who has made him known' (v. 18). People frequently ask, 'How do you know there is a God? You can't see him.' 'How do you know what God is like?' The crucial answer to these legitimate questions is, 'Because of Jesus'. There's plenty of evidence besides Jesus to point us in the right direction, but he is the decisive revelation. He has made the invisible God visible, as he told his disciples (John 14:8–9). What we can only surmise about God elsewhere becomes a sure thing in Jesus. In Archbishop Michael Ramsey's words, 'God is Christlike and in him there is no unChristlikeness at all.'[55]

John is going to unpack what he writes in condensed form here throughout his Gospel. And all the time he's concerned to say, 'We didn't make this up. "We have seen his glory" with our own eyes.'

Enjoy the meal!

For reflection

Whoever has seen me has seen the Father.
JOHN 14:9

2 January

Firstborn of all creation

In him all things in heaven and on earth were created, things visible and invisible, whether thrones or dominions or rulers or powers – all things have been created through him and for him.
COLOSSIANS 1:16

Read Colossians 1:15–17.

While you can visit the sites of most churches mentioned in the New Testament, you won't find Colossae on the normal tourist track, and with good reason. Colossae, a little town which made its living from sheep farming, never enjoyed a secure existence and was somewhat overshadowed by more impressive cities nearby.[56] It suffered a number of misfortunes and was destroyed by an earthquake in AD60–61, around the time of Paul's letter to them.

To the Colossians, the world was a precarious place and that's the clue to understanding what Paul emphasises to them about Jesus. Their experience suggested all sorts of turbulent powers inhabited the world, and many of these were out to harm them. They went under various titles and were both of a seen and unseen variety. It was as if there was a tear in the fabric of the universe and all sorts of alien powers had been able to enter their world through it. Jews and Gentiles alike sought protection from these powers through their religious practices and many did a belt-and-braces job by praying to lots of different deities at once. The Jewish folk in particular sought protection through angels, with Michael being the chief among them. Paul writes that such an approach is futile, misguided and unnecessary. If they had really understood the gospel of Jesus Christ, and who he was, they wouldn't be looking for answers elsewhere. He was all they needed. Believers in Jesus as the Christ really needed to follow through on the faith they confessed in him.

So it was that Paul wrote to this ordinary bunch of sheep farmers and market traders some of the most exalted theology about Jesus you'll find anywhere in the New Testament. He doesn't claim anything new for Jesus. What he writes is what we read in John 1, Hebrews 1 and elsewhere. Yet he applies it in new ways.

Jesus is not one among a conglomeration of supposed powers; he is altogether superior and different. Today's reading spells out his uniqueness in four areas.

- He is *unique in his relation to God* as 'the image of the invisible God', as we saw John explain. Adam was made in the image of God, but through sin that image was corrupted. In Jesus the image is untainted, giving us a true picture of God himself and of humanity as God intended it to be.
- He is *unique in his position in creation*. By 'the firstborn' Paul does not mean he was born before anyone else, but that, like the firstborn in an ancient family, he is in the unrivalled position of honour above others in the family. So Jesus is in the position of supreme honour in the universe, with all creation bowing to him.
- He is *unique in his hold on power*. The Colossians feared that there were powers out to destroy them and prayed to other powers to protect them, but there was only one power who counted and that was Jesus. And that was because…
- He is *unique in his role in creation*. Resonating with John, Paul tells us that he created all things but then adds that the world not only came into being 'through him' but also 'for him'. He is both the source and the goal of creation. And this isn't just about past or future history. It is about what Jesus is doing in creation now, since 'in him all things hold together' because of his continuing

providential involvement in it. Without him, the world would spiral into chaos. He gives it order and preserves it from degeneration.

What is astounding about these claims is that they are made about the man Jesus of Nazareth, who not long before, in the lifetime of many who were still alive, had lived among them, travelled with them, eaten with them, laughed and cried with them, taught them, and then been crucified. The same people who saw all that, also claimed that they'd seen him alive again, after three days. Once they'd understood it, the resurrection was proof enough for them that there was no greater power than him in the universe, neither the power of sin, nor death, nor Satan, nor the Jewish religion, nor Rome. It was not that the resurrection gave him new powers, but that it demonstrated the power that had rightly been his all along, power that was inherent in his being 'the firstborn'. If the claims were not true, the early Christians were delusional. But the Colossians could easily test them out for themselves, as can we. What was needed was that they pursued the risky logic of their faith and relied exclusively on Christ, the strongest power in creation.

For reflection

From the rising of the sun
   and from the west... there is no one besides me;
   I am the Lord, and there is no other.
ISAIAH 45:6

3 January

The pre-eminent one

... so that he might come to have first place in everything.
COLOSSIANS 1:18

Read Colossians 1:18–20.

'Hang on, Paul. Not so fast,' one can imagine the Colossians responding. 'All these claims about Christ and creation are all very well, but my world is still hazardous and unstable. The "powers" still seem to be at large. What have you got to say about that?' Paul would agree and that's why he, like many a teacher responding to a pupil's urgent question, might have replied, 'You hang on. I'm coming to that. I've only told you the first part of the story, so far.'

For all its order, the physical world seems to face a fair degree of disjointedness and the human world even more disharmony. But God has a plan and is in the process of sorting it out. And Jesus is the absolutely central key to it. Paul's explanation, even more audacious than anything he has said until now, closely weaves five things together: church, resurrection, fullness, reconciliation and cross.

The small group of Jesus' followers in Colossae were not incidental to God's rescue plan but a vital part of it. Although physically absent from earth himself, Jesus had called a body of people into existence which he presides over as head. The *church* is the herald of the reconciled creation to come, as is more fully explained in Ephesians 2. They are the people through whom he announces the good news of a new creation where alien powers have no part. They not only talk about it but also live it, though imperfectly, in the light of the re-creation to come.

Sure, these people will die, like everyone else. So, doesn't death still have its hold over creation? How do we know it has been defeated? Because, says Paul, Jesus is not only the firstborn in creation but 'the firstborn from the dead'. His *resurrection* isn't the only one that is going to take place but it was the first one, which others will replicate. His resurrection set the pattern for our own future resurrections. Elsewhere Paul speaks of Jesus' resurrection as 'the first fruits of those who have died' (1 Corinthians 15:20). First fruits or firstborn makes little difference. There's no one who beats him to it, since he is the head of the queue of those who one day will experience their own life after life.

How could this be? There's one thing we need to know about Jesus that makes all the difference. Even if the other 'thrones, dominions, rulers and powers' to which the Colossians credited power had some divine touch about them – and we're not saying they did – they fell far short of God himself. At best, they were feeble intermediaries between God and people. In sharp contrast, God in all his *fullness*, in all his totality, was pleased to inhabit in Jesus. Jesus was fully and completely the revelation of God and the agent of his salvation. Some years ago, F.F. Bruce summed it up like this: 'He is the one mediator between God and the world of mankind, and all the attributes and activities of God – His spirit, word, wisdom and glory – are displayed in Him.'[57] Since this is so, we need not turn to any lesser power for help or salvation.

The purpose of God's power in him is that he might 'reconcile to himself all things, whether on earth or in heaven'. The problem with the present creation is that it is out of alignment with God. *Reconciliation* is about restoring people and things to their proper relationship with God. The Christian hope is that God will do just that, knitting our fractured world together again and healing the brokenness of our present creation. Paul explained to the Ephesians that this would happen when everything is gathered up by Christ (Ephesians 1:10) and put back into its proper place under God's rule. It's like a parent restoring order to a chaotic bedroom after a child and his friends have been playing with their toys, leaving them strewn out of place; only on a cosmic scale. The child may not cooperate in the exercise! Nor should we assume that Paul's vision of cosmic reconciliation means everyone will voluntarily return to God. In Paul's day, Rome could impose reconciliation as well as woo people to it. In the end, Paul is saying, God's rule will triumph and peace will be restored.

Paul was more concerned to point out to the Colossians that this reconciliation happens 'through the blood of his *cross*'. It is an audacious vision of the cross. The cross not only reconciles individuals to God but is also the means by which the whole of creation will be reborn. Because of the cross 'the disharmonies of nature and the inhumanities of humankind'[58] will be resolved. His death is the way that new life will come to all creation.

In whatever direction you look, then, in the past, present and future, in creation, in things seen and unseen, or in the church, Jesus Christ is the pre-eminent one, supreme over all. 'The vision is vast. The claim is mind-blowing.'[59] And it compels our worship.

For reflection:

Blessed be his glorious name for ever;
   may his glory fill the whole earth.
Amen and amen.
PSALM 72:19

4 January

God has spoken

But in these last days [God] has spoken to us by a Son...
HEBREWS 1:1

Read Hebrews 1:1–2.

Much was made of the fact that when Donald Trump was elected president of the United States, the British prime minister was the ninth world leader he rang. Did not 'the special relationship' demand she was higher up on his list than that? Or was it true that they couldn't find the phone number to No 10? No doubt Theresa May had plenty to occupy her and didn't spend hours pacing up and down the Cabinet Room waiting for the call. How many hours of our lives, I wonder, do we spend waiting for the call, whether it's the call from the plumber, the doctor, the supplier, or our daughter or son? Some even search the skies in the hope of making contact with some extraterrestrial being and wondering whether there is anyone out there. Communication matters to us.

As human beings we're wired for communication, maybe because we are created in God's image and he is a communicating God. When Hebrews sets out to explain to wavering, doubtful Christians the awesome superiority of the Christ to anything they had encountered in their religious experience before, it begins with God speaking. Two important aspects of God's communication emerge in the opening verses of the letter: God's message is final and God's message is personal.

God's message is final. With a deft series of contrasting strokes,[60] the writer portrays exactly his readers' situation. The first contrast is about time: then and now. God spoke 'long ago' but has spoken again 'in these last days'. He did not only speak in the past but has spoken recently and, as we shall see, remarkably. God is not simply a God of the past but a God of the present. He is not the great 'I was' but the great 'I am'.

The second contrast is about his audience: them and us. 'Our ancestors' heard his voice in their own day but contemporary listeners have heard his voice as well. What an amazing, if somewhat terrifying, privilege it is that God addresses us. The writer later warns his readers not to make the mistake of their ancestors who heard his voice in the wilderness but failed to profit from it because they stubbornly refused to believe it (Hebrews 4:1–11).

The third contrast is about the means of his communication: various versus one. 'In former times... he spoke in fragmentary and varied fashion through the prophets' (NEB). In many respects that was a good thing. The sending of so many prophets testified to the abundance of God's love for his people and his desire to direct them to what were the right paths for their own day. But each of them only spoke a partial message and none had the final word. Now, though, God has spoken through one channel a message that is complete in itself and never to be overtaken. God's speaking was 'no garbled message, muted voice or unintelligible sound; it was clear and trustworthy...'[61] These were 'the last days', the penultimate chapter of God's salvation plan before the ultimate chapter of the return of Christ and re-creation of all things (Hebrews 9:28). So there will be no future revelation to amend, improve or surpass what has been heard in Christ.

The fourth contrast is about the messenger: prophets versus the Son. Prophets were human beings, called and empowered by the Spirit to be God's spokespersons in the world. The Son was the same and yet was different from them. He was not less than they were, but he was so much more. They stood in relation to God as servants who played a minor role. He stood in relation to God as a Son who would eclipse all others. In setting out these contrasts, the author is not meaning to write the past off as unimportant but rather the opposite – to say that all the past led up to this. Christ, the fullest communication of God to his world came 'at the end of the age' (Hebrews 9:26). He fulfilled all that the former days had pointed to, whether in the law, the covenants, the temple, the priesthood or, yes, in the prophecies as well.

God's message is personal. We rate the value of a communication partly by the form in which it comes to us. A short, impersonal printed letter from a bureaucrat doesn't rate nearly as highly as a personal, handwritten letter. Were we to get a message from the Queen, it would rate highly indeed. Truth to tell, though, we conspire in a fiction since we know she didn't actually command it to be sent personally or sign it individually. If, however, she were to send one of the royal princes to us with a message, that would be different! So it is with God. His final messenger is none other than his Son, the one who is in a unique relationship with him. Looking forward, this Son, like any son in the ancient world, was to be his father's heir. However, unlike any human son who might inherit a greater or lesser fortune (or even some debts!) this son will inherit the entire universe, becoming ruler over it all. Looking back, along with John and Paul, Hebrews asserts that it was Jesus 'through whom [God] created the worlds'. Now that's a messenger worth listening to!

For reflection

> He said to me, 'You are my son;
>   today I have begotten you.
> Ask of me, and I will make the nations your heritage,
>   and the ends of the earth your possession.'
> PSALM 2:7–8

5 January

The radiance of God's glory

He is the reflection of God's glory and the exact imprint of God's very being…
HEBREWS 1:3

Read Hebrews 1:2–4.

My wife is one of those people who love lists. So, let's not beat about the bush; here's a list about Jesus. F.F. Bruce pointed out that in these verses 'seven facts are stated about the Son of God which bring out His greatness and show why the revelation given in Him is the highest that God can give'.[62] Seven facts, note – seven being the symbolic number for completeness and perfection.

We have already mentioned the first two: **1** God has appointed his Son 'heir of all things'; **2** 'he also created the worlds'. What are the other facts?

3 'He is the reflection of God's glory'. Actually, reflection plays it down a little bit. The word is more alive than that and means 'brightness' or 'radiance'. The majestic, transcendent glory of God himself shines out from Jesus. It may not have dazzled people, as it did when Isaiah went to the temple or when Ezekiel encountered it in his visions. There may only have been one occasion during Jesus' lifetime when his closest disciples saw it as it really was, on the Mount of Transfiguration (Mark 9:2–8). Mostly the glory was filtered, and that was just as well because human beings cannot look directly into the glory of God and live (Exodus 33:17–23), any more than human beings can look directly into the sun without somehow shielding their eyes. So, God accommodates himself to our human limitations and displays his glory in ways which are appropriate to us. It was glory, nonetheless.

4 'The exact imprint of God's very being.' The author chooses his words very carefully. Jesus is not a rough reflection of God, but 'the express image of his person' (AV), 'the exact representation of his being' (NIV) or, in Tom Wright's translation, 'the precise expression of his (God's) own being'.[63] He's not more or less like God but accurately and reliably reveals God in the world. Commenting on this, Wright says, 'He is, dare we say it, not just a chip off the old block – as though there might be many such people, perfectly reflecting God's own inner being – but the unique son. Look at him, and it's like looking in a mirror at God himself. His character is exactly reproduced, plain to see.'[64]

Many suggest that the author of Hebrews would have been familiar with a book called the Wisdom of Solomon and may, at least unconsciously, have been borrowing from it or in conversation with it here. When it spoke of Lady Wisdom it said:

For she is the breath of the power of God,
and a pure emanation of the glory of the Almighty;
therefore nothing defiled gains entrance to her.
For she is a reflection of eternal light,
a spotless mirror of the working of God,
and an image of his goodness.
WISDOM OF SOLOMON 7:25–26

What this earlier writing reached for in talking about the idea of Wisdom, Hebrews says has become a reality in the person of Christ.

5 'He sustains all things by his powerful word.' This is the same claim we met in Paul's celebration of Christ as the creator who holds all

things together (Colossians 1:17). As his word brought creation into being originally, so now creation continues to depend on his word, or else it would collapse. It is 'in him we live and move and have our being' (Acts 17:28). He providentially rules over all.

6   'He... made purification for sins.' The focus shifts from Jesus as the creator to Jesus as the Saviour.[65] Given that the readership of this letter is primarily Jewish, 'so great a salvation' (v. 3) is explained in terms they'd be familiar with. Sin stains and needs to be cleansed. The way to be cleansed is through the offering of a blood sacrifice. Jesus sacrificed himself in an offering that rendered all lesser offerings redundant: 'he has appeared once for all at the end of the age to remove sin by the sacrifice of himself' (Hebrews 9:26, which is explained further in 10:1–18).

7   'He sat down at the right hand of the Majesty on high.' Having accomplished his work of salvation, he is 'crowned with glory and honour' (Hebrews 2:9) and promoted to a throne alongside the throne of God in heaven. The writer's concern is not with where heaven is but with what heaven symbolises. Jesus assumes his place at the control centre of creation, where God's sovereignty is being exercised even if we do not yet see everything under his control (Hebrews 2:9). But we've not reached the end of the story yet: 'Christ was sacrificed once to take away the sins of many; and he will appear a second time, not to bear sin, but to bring salvation to those who are waiting for him' (Hebrews 9:28, NIV).

This condensed list, supported by seven quotations from the Old Testament (vv. 5–14), sets the agenda for the rest of the letter. It's going to take 13 chapters to unpack it all for these Jewish believers, and even then the author claims he has only 'written... briefly' (Hebrews 13:22). Jesus is so great that even this only begins to explain the one who astonishingly was born a baby in Bethlehem.

For reflection

The Lord says to my lord,
  'Sit at my right hand
until I make your enemies your footstool.'
PSALM 110:1

6 January

Worship Jesus

When they saw him, they worshipped him...
MATTHEW 28:17

**And again, when he brings the firstborn into the world,
he says, 'Let all God's angels worship him.'**
HEBREWS 1:6

What made early Christianity unique was that it centred on the worship of Jesus. That's what the pagans constantly said about it. Christians did not merely think of Jesus as a man with an unusually developed sense of God or refined sense of morality, a wise teacher, or a compassionate doer of good. They would have agreed with all that, but it may only have led them to a humanistic idea about him. They went way beyond that in their estimate of him. They worshipped him. They prayed to him, praised him, expressed devotion to him, experienced wonder at him and bowed in obedience to him. They adored him in the way reserved only for God himself. It is utterly astonishing that good Jewish monotheists, who from their earliest days believed there was only one God, came now to worship Jesus, the baby of Bethlehem and man of Nazareth, and to place him 'unequivocally within the unique divine' being.[66]

The Christmas story hints at what was to come. Having heard the angels sing, the shepherds immediately went to check out their message. We're not told they took any lambs with them as a gift or how they handled themselves while with Mary and Joseph, but when they left, they couldn't stop 'glorifying and praising God for all they had heard and seen', and they couldn't stop talking about it either (Luke 2:15–20). When the wise men from the East finally tracked Jesus down to Bethlehem they went further than the shepherds. 'They knelt down and paid him homage' (Matthew 2:11). Both that, and the gifts they gave him, went well beyond any normal behaviour that might be expected on the birth of a child, especially one born into such an ordinary family they had no personal connection with.

As the work of Jesus unfolds, more and more people express belief in him and offer devotion to him. Matthew, in particular, records people prostrating themselves before Jesus and offering him greater-than-usual admiration.[67] But it wasn't until after the resurrection that all the clues fell into place and some, at least, worked it out and so unreservedly worshipped him. On meeting the risen Christ, the disciples 'took hold of his feet, and worshipped him' (Matthew 28:9), as they were to do again days later as he took his leave of them (Matthew 28:17). From then on, the early Christians blended the worship of Jesus with the worship of God and made it central in all they did.

Let's look at two witnesses who support that. First, Hebrews. Hebrews seems fixated with angels; they're mentioned six times in the first chapter alone. But since they figure so much in the Christmas story, it is worth returning to them as we come to conclude our glimpses through the keyholes of scripture onto the baby Christ. The angels are instructed to worship Jesus as he is enthroned (Hebrews 1:6). Angels played a significant role in synagogue worship at the time, but they were never worshipped, or if they were it was illegitimate. By instructing them to worship Jesus, Hebrews is categorically putting him in a class of his own above them. Jesus is not one of them, a mere messenger from God, however powerful. He's not semi-divine or a little superior to them but absolutely superior, deserving the worship which is reserved for God alone.[68]

The second witness is the book of Revelation, chapters 4 and 5, where John gives us yet another look through the keyhole so that we glimpse what is happening behind the scenes of the conflicted world we live in. Having described the throne of God and what is going on around it, John then focuses on the one at the right hand of God, who is unmistakably Jesus, the victorious lion who is at the same time a slain lamb. Those present at the throne, the four living creatures (representing all that is best in creation) and the twenty-four elders (representing the people of God down the centuries), 'fell before the Lamb' and sang 'a new song' declaring that he is 'worthy'. Before long, the swelling choir of creation who declare the lamb worthy 'to receive power and wealth and wisdom and might and honour and glory and blessing!' join them. That truly is worship.

Our glimpses through the keyholes of the Christmas story have given us sight of far, far more than a young, vulnerable couple who gave birth to a baby in an uncertain world and laid him in a manger. Through these keyholes, we have seen how the whole story of Israel is coming to its fulfilment as God sends his Son to be the Saviour of the world. He truly meets the hopes and longings of many generations. The keyholes open up vistas not only on to Israel's past story but also to Israel's and indeed the world's future story. We see this baby grow to a man, die on a cross and rise from the dead, and we look forward to him coming again. We perceive this baby to be none other than the creator of the cosmos, and the one through whom the cosmos is being rescued and will one day be remade.

Such a child is to be adored. Such a Saviour is to be worshipped. Nothing short of that will do.

For reflection

'To the one seated on the throne and to the Lamb
be blessing and honour and glory and might
for ever and ever!'
And the four living creatures said, 'Amen!' And the elders fell
down and worshipped.

REVELATION 5:13–14

Notes

1 For those who may wish to explore the topic of the Old Testament roots of the Christian faith, I thoroughly recommend Chris Wright, *Knowing Jesus through the Old Testament* (IVP, 1995).

2 This sentence is greatly influenced by J.I. Packer's classic comment in *Knowing God* (Hodder and Stoughton, 1973), p. 18 (emphasis in original): 'How can we turn our knowledge *about* God into knowledge *of* God? The rule for doing this is demanding but simple. It is that we turn each truth that we learn *about* God into a matter of meditation *before* God, leading to prayer and praise *to* God.'

3 John White, *People in Prayer* (IVP, 1977), p. 85.

4 Adapted from A. Bengal, cited in James R. Edwards, *The Gospel according to Luke* (Apollos, 2015), p. 45.

5 *Romeo and Juliet*, Act II, sc. ii.

6 *The Merchant of Venice*, Act IV, sc. i.

7 C.S. Lewis, *Mere Christianity* (Fontana, 1955), pp. 106, 108.

8 Joel Green, *The Theology of the Gospel of Luke* (CUP, 1995), p. 82. See Green's full discussion, pp. 76–101.

9 Eugene H. Peterson, *A Long Obedience in the Same Direction* (IVP, 2000), 2nd ed. pp. 86–87.

10 Peterson, *A Long Obedience*, pp. 86–87.

11 This figure, for 2010, comes from the respected Pew Foundation.

12 Much contemporary scholarship finds it difficult to believe the prophets had the ability to foresee the future and therefore argues that their words were actually spoken after the events they appear to predict and written up as if they were spoken beforehand. But this is an ideological position which is philosophically required only if you do not believe in a God who engages with his world both naturally and supernaturally. If one accepts that Jesus rose from the dead, then believing in predictive prophecy is no great difficulty.

13 No single Old Testament quotation seems to fit the bill but some have seen this as a word play on Isaiah 11:1 where the word 'branch' in Hebrew is *neser*.

14 See also 1:45, 5:46; 7:40.

15 Peter J. Gentry and Stephen J. Wellum, *Kingdom and Covenant: A biblical-theological understanding of the covenants* (Crossway, 2012), p. 141.

16 Gentry and Wellum, *Kingdom and Covenant*, p. 297.
17 Edwards, *The Gospel according to Luke*, p. 62.
18 As mentioned in the comment on 6 December, there is a place for fear in the sense of respect but not for fear in the sense of being afraid of someone, as is meant here.
19 I owe this point to Edwards, *The Gospel according to Luke*, p. 63.
20 Morna D. Hooker, *The Message of Mark* (Epworth Press, 1983), p. 9.
21 See Luke 3:3; 4:18; 5:20–21, 23–24; 7:48–49; 11:4; 17:4 and 23:34.
22 'Light' in *Dictionary of Biblical Imagery*, eds. Leylan Ryken, James C. Wilhoit, Temper Longman III (IVP, 1998), p. 509.
23 Cited in Paula Gooder, *Heaven* (SPCK, 2011), p. 32.
24 Gooder, *Heaven*, p. 33.
25 See further Gooder, *Heaven*, passim, and Tom Wright, *Surprised by Hope* (SPCK, 2007), p. 122.
26 'Glory' in *Dictionary of Biblical Imagery*, p. 330.
27 Philip Yancey, *The Jesus I Never Knew* (Marshall Pickering, 1995), p. 34.
28 J.F. Maile, 'Heaven' in *Dictionary of Paul and his Letters*, eds. Gerald F. Hawthorne, Ralph P. Martin and Daniel G. Reid (IVP, 1993), p. 381.
29 For a full exposition of this theme see the author's *Called by God: Exploring our Identity in Christ* (Oxford: BRF, 2017), ch. 7.
30 David Atkinson, *Peace in our Time* (Eerdmans, 1985), p. 137.
31 The source for this was probably the influential Vulgate translation.
32 John Calvin, *A Harmony of the Gospels* (St Andrews Press, 1972), trans. A.W. Morrison, p. 78.
33 Luke Timothy Johnson, *The Gospel of Luke* (Liturgical Press, 1991), p. 51.
34 Calvin, *Harmony of the Gospels*, p. 78.
35 Joel B. Green, *The Gospel of Luke* (Eerdmans, 1997), p. 137.
36 Calvin, *Harmony of the Gospels*, p. 78.
37 C.H. Spurgeon, *The Treasury of the Bible, New Testament*, vol. 1 (Marshall, Morgan and Scott, 1962), p. 641.
38 Spurgeon, *The Treasury of the Bible, New Testament*, vol. 1, p. 641.
39 The song is called the Nunc dimittis which is the Latin for its first words, 'Now, dismiss… '
40 Details can be found in Edwards, *The Gospel according to Luke*, p. 83.
41 I. Howard Marshall, *The Gospel of Luke* (Paternoster Press, 1978), p. 118.
42 Max Turner, *Power from on High: The Spirit in Israel's restoration and witness in Luke-Acts* (Sheffield Academic Press, 1996), p. 149.